ADVANCES IN COMPUTER CHESS
2

M. R. B. CLARKE

Editor

Edinburgh
University Press

© 1980
Edinburgh University Press
22 George Square, Edinburgh
ISBN 0 85224 377 4
Printed in Great Britain by
Redwood Burn Limited
Trowbridge & Esher

CONTENTS

PREFACE

This, the second volume in a series devoted entirely to computer chess, reports the proceedings of a meeting held at Edinburgh University in April 1978.

Introducing the first of the series we put forward the view that chess is a promising experimental system within which to study the implications of computing with knowledge rather than numbers. Many of the papers in this volume follow the theme closely, and a further encouraging sign of the validity of this view is that a significant proportion of the work reported here has been supported by the Science Research Council.

More unexpected perhaps is the contribution to chess theory itself that computer analysis is making. No serious player, even among those not primarily interested in artificial intelligence, can fail to be stimulated by the insight into endgame theory that computation is opening up, and although this work was originally seen as being mainly of interest to computer scientists many well-known players have taken a strong interest and we feel that many of the papers in this book have as much to offer the active player as the theoretician.

The meeting itself would not have been possible without the generous financial support of I.B.M. (UK) Ltd., I.C.L. Ltd., *Computer Weekly*, and *The Times* and *Sunday Times*. Invaluable help with logistics and computing equipment was given by the Atomic Energy Research Establishment, Harwell, the Edinburgh Regional Computing Centre, Edinburgh University Department of Computer Science, and in particular Professor Donald Michie and his staff at the Edinburgh University Machine Intelligence Research Unit. Once again it is a pleasure to thank the Edinburgh University Press for their usual high standard of production and co-operation.

The Construction of
Economical and Correct Algorithms for
King and Pawn against King

D.F.Beal and M.R.B.Clarke

Our starting point is the idea that the scientific way to study problems like chess programming is not to look at heuristic methods that often give the wrong answer, but by analogy with other combinatorial problems (treating chess as computation of the game-theoretic value) to study the properties of algorithms that always return the correct value.

A good analogy to bear in mind is an example used by Dijkstra (1972) in the book *Structured Programming*. A table of prime numbers is not just a table of arbitrary numbers. There are simple algorithms for computing it, which are undoubtedly correct because they embody a clear mathematical definition. There are also heuristic programs that attempt to calculate primes, leaving unknown which of the numbers output actually are prime. Where exact algorithms are computationally feasible they are naturally preferred. Even for heuristic programs some exact guarantee is valuable (e.g. this number may not be prime but it has no factors of less than eight digits), which may be regarded as finding an exact algorithm for a clearly defined modification of the problem. Similarly, we would prefer exact programs for chess functions.

For the simplest chess endgames a clear exact algorithm (systematic valuing of every position) is just computationally feasible. Our work has been to seek ways of constructing more compact algorithms without relaxing the requirement of proving them correct.

King and pawn against king (KPK) is the simplest ending requiring non-trivial concepts for its solution; only the best human players are perfect evaluators over the whole space, which, reflections and redundancies removed, consists of 98304 distinct configurations. The analogue of the table of prime numbers is the database, Clarke (1977), that labels each of these configurations draw or win in a specified number of moves, obtained by reversed minimaxing (backing-up) from primitive terminal positions. Such a table enables a simple program to be written to play perfectly, whose time complexity is small but whose space complexity is correspondingly large (the simple forward minimax method of evaluation is at the other end of the time/store trade-off axis). Similar databases have now been constructed for a number of more complicated endings, notably by Ken Thompson at Bell Labs and Arlazarov and Futer (1979) in Moscow. These tables are, of course, very large and the method soon becomes as space bound as simple minimaxing is timebound.

Conventional programs written for this ending in a high-level language include those of Tan (1972) and Harris (1977), which, using little or no stored data, are more or less direct attempts to encode knowledge obtained from books or personal experience. Bramer (1977b) and Beal (1977 and appendix 5 of this paper) have constructed programs consisting of simple search routines accessing a position evaluator, which is based on a hierarchy of functions and predicates developed and refined by interaction with expert players or stored databases. Michalski and Negri (1977) have described a program that starts with a repertoire of useful-looking predicates and a sample of positions whose value is known and builds up descriptions of winning positions in terms of these.

The Tan and Harris programs are, as far as we know, strong but by no means completely correct; those of Bramer and Beal are known to be correct but only as a result of comparison with the database over the entire set of legal positions. Programs stated to be nearly correct may nevertheless contain 'pockets' of completely unsound play. Only the simple search program that directly accesses the database can be said in any sense to be 'correct by construction', and this of course is at the extremely bulky end of the time/store trade-off axis.

In a previous paper (Clarke 1977) a rather simple-minded diagram was used to illustrate the relationship between search-based and data-based programs. Figure 1 is an elaboration of that diagram with an extra dimension for program correctness. The slope from the origin up on to the plateau of fully correct play represents the trade-off as it is currently known between economy and correctness for conventionally written computer programs; programs such as Tan's (1972) lie somewhere on this slope. The metaphor seems appropriate because standing on such a convex hill it is hard to know how much further you have to go to get to the top. Will such programs grow indefinitely to database dimensions as they are finally made perfectly correct?

A rough estimate of where the top of the hill is can be obtained by constructing a standard 'naive' program. Suppose for simplicity all positions to be either won for one side or drawn, so that the game is only two-valued, as in KPK or KRKN, and suppose that we require the program to always respond correctly to a request for a value within time T. Let the average branching factor with randomly ordered alpha-beta search be b (= real branching factor raised to the power 0.75), and let the processing time per node be t.

Then the maximum search depth i is given by $T = tb^i$ approximately, and the values of positions lying deeper than this will have to be based on stored material. We suppose these to be stored explicitly; another search to depth i would involve storing the values of many terminal nodes.

To make further progress we need an assumption about the shape of the tree. Suppose the number of positions at depth j to be of the form na^j, where $a < 1$ and n is the total number of possible configurations (and hence the size of a complete database. This form is neither particularly well nor particularly badly fitted by KPK and KRKN). It follows that the number of positions to be stored is $S = na^i$, and so $(T/t)(S/n)^p = 1$, where $p = -\log b / \log a$ is a positive constant characteristic of the ending, providing some justification for the hyperbolic shape of the trade-off curve in figure 1.

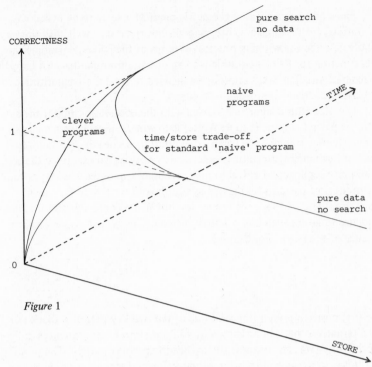

Figure 1

Programs in the 'correctness = 1' plane to the origin side of this curve are less naive than the standard, the only known examples being the Bramer and Beal routines. Note that these have had to get there from the wrong side of the curve by relying on the database for verification. Our aim is to study methods of constructing correct programs that do not rely on this.

One approach to saving space whilst retaining optimality is to try to map the complete state space onto a smaller set of functionally equivalent patterns, backing up from the very simple predicates that describe terminal nodes to force evaluation of more complex patterns. However, trying to follow this through in detail we found led to an unmanageable proliferation of patterns if the goal of generating a provably correct evaluator was to be retained. More detail and some examples are given in appendix 4.

Nevertheless, even if this idea is abandoned, we thought it of interest to see if a perfect evaluator could be constructed by relaxing the requirement for deduction as a method of verification and instead using the database. One of us (Beal) constructed a Fortran function of about 120 statements embodying 48 logical tests of geometric features, which discriminates perfectly between wins and draws over the whole space. The method was an iterative process of comparing the values returned by the function against the database for every position, noting features that they had in common and debugging the code in an essentially *ad hoc* though methodical way. The complete text of this program and some further details are given in appendix 5. In more complex situations the database is too large for this method to be available.

Since quite complicated geometric predicates seem to be necessary for optimal evaluation, and since these do not agree very well with the way people describe the winning process (in terms of the Dijkstra example the Beal function for KPK is equivalent to an obscure formula that just happens to generate the first 5000 primes), we decided to try a more algorithmic and less data-driven approach.

Our algorithmic approach started with the observation that if the side with the pawn (suppose it to be White) is to win, he must have a method of repeatedly advancing the pawn safely until it reaches the 8th rank. Instead of beginning with static geometric descriptions we examined the set of all move sequences. Central to many winning sequences were repeating occurrences of patterns (expressed as coordinates relative to the pawn). Black's replies could vary the sequences, but White could always force the sequence to go through one or other of two particular patterns with each advance of the pawn. For example:

```
. . . . .    . . . . .    . . . . .    . . . . .    . . . B .    . . . B .    . . B . .
. . B . .    . . B . .    . . . B .    . . B . .    . . . . .    . . . . .    . . . . .
. . . . .    . . . . .    . . . . .    . W . . .    . . W . .    . . W . .    . . W . .
. W . . .    . . W . .    . . W . .    . . . . .    . . . . .    . . P . .    . . P . .
. . . P . .    . . P . .    . . P . .    . . P . .    . . P . .    . . . . .    . . . . .
```

The first position is an instance of one of the two key patterns. Black (B) has alternatives that can be shown to lead only into other sequences in which White (W) can continue to advance the pawn (P) safely. The proof that this is so uses a combination of induction and enumeration, in the sense in which Dijkstra uses the words when demonstrating that programs do what they are supposed to. Details are given in appendix 2.

Not many positions match the two key patterns, of course, and for positions that do not analysis is required to determine whether an 'initializing' sequence (one forcing a key pattern) is available to White. In many cases one king is obviously nearer to critical squares, and we present (appendix 3) some definitions that make this idea precise. From them are derived, and proved correct, extensions to the key patterns. The extended patterns match positions in which White can force the key pattern by an initializing sequence. The simpler ideas of White running the pawn and Black capturing it are also covered by patterns proved correct in the same ways.

The algorithm values positions by comparing them with its set of patterns: if the position matches one of them the value is known, if not a search is necessary. This search should be small for all positions. We believe that when the algorithm is complete (see next paragraph) it will be possible to derive precise upper bounds on the size of the search.

Not yet included in the algorithm are key patterns for Black to draw (in particular those where the pawn is on the rook's file). We anticipate no difficulty in doing this as we think we have already tackled the most difficult cases and established sufficient concepts. The current state of the algorithm is described in appendix 1; proofs of correctness are in appendixes 2 and 3.

Although this is the first attempt we know of to prove a program for KPK it should be noted that Bratko (1978) has proved correct a complete algorithm for king and rook against king (a considerably less subtle ending), his formal basis being Michie's (1976) Advice Language AL1.

There are strong similarities between the process of analysing the move sequences to yield patterns with provable values, and with a structured approach to many conventional programming tasks. The common feature seems to be that analysis of the problem suggested a simple *repeat . . . until . . .* structure where the relevant predicate could be proved invariant over the loop by a careful enumeration of cases.

We drew an analogy earlier with computations involving prime numbers. We can return to it by pointing to a series of papers, the most recent of which is by Gries and Misra (1978), in which substantial improvements to an old algorithm (the sieve of Eratosthenes) have resulted not from new programming tricks but from new lemmas about primes suggested by the fresh ways of looking at old problems that programming often requires. We believe that good chess programs will be similar, in being well-structured embodiments of new theorems about the geometry of the game and more generally about the effects of certain kinds of tree searches.

ACKNOWLEDGEMENT
We would like to acknowledge the support of the Science Research Council for this work.

REFERENCES
Arlazarov, V.L. & A.L. Futer (1979) Computer analysis of a rook end game, in *Machine Intelligence 9* (ed. Hayes, Michie & Mikulich). Horwood/ Wiley (in press).

Beal, D.F. (1977) *Discriminating wins from draws in KPK*. Report, Dept Computer Science, Queen Mary College, London University (reprinted here as appendix 5).

Bramer, M.A. (1977a) *King and pawn against king: using effective distance.* Report; Open University, Milton Keynes.

———(1977b) *Representation of knowledge for chess endgames: towards a self-improving system.* PhD Thesis; Open University, Milton Keynes.

Bratko, I. (1978) Proving correctness of strategies in the AL1 assertional language. *Information Processing Letters 5*, 223-30.

Clarke, M.R.B. (1977) A quantitative study of king and pawn against king, in *Advances in Computer Chess 1* (ed. M.R.B. Clarke). Edinburgh University Press.

Dahl, O.J., E.W. Dijkstra & C.A.R. Hoare (1972) *Structured Programming.* Academic Press.

Gries, D. & J. Misra (1978) A linear sieve algorithm for finding prime numbers. *CACM 21*, 12, 999-1003.

Harris, L.R. (1977) Listing of Algol 60 program circulated privately.

Michalski, R.S. & P.G. Negri (1977) An experiment on inductive learning in chess end games, in *Machine Intelligence 8* (eds Elcock & Michie) pp. 175-92. Ellis Horwood/Wiley.

Michie, D. (1976) An advice-taking system for computer chess. *Computer Bulletin* (ser. 2) *10*, 12-14.

Tan, S.T. (1972) *Representation of knowledge for very simple pawn endings in chess*. Report MIP-R-98; School of Artificial Intelligence, Edinburgh University.

Appendix 1. An Algorithm for KPK

This algorithm decides, for a given KPK position with White to play, whether it is a win or draw. Many such, or similar, algorithms already exist (Beal 1977, Bramer 1977b, Clarke 1977, Harris 1977, Piasetski 1977, Tan 1972), two of which (Beal's and Bramer's) are known to be perfectly correct by exhaustive comparison with Clarke's, which is a complete catalogue of KPK positions. This one differs in attempting to be provably correct from its structure, without using a complete catalogue either during its construction or for testing its outputs afterwards. Moreover, our aim was the automatic construction of at least parts of the algorithm, although this has yet to be done.

Central to the organization of the algorithm is the concept of representing most of the wins in terms of repetitive move sequences and initializing move sequences.

By a repetitive move sequence we mean one where a little bit of king manoeuvring enables the pawn to safely advance one square, after which the original pattern of the pieces is or can be restored and the sequence repeated. For example (B = black king, W = white king, P = white pawn. White to play):

```
. . . . .    . . . . .    . . . . .    . . . B .    . . . B .    . . B . .
. . B . .    . . B . .    . . . B .    . . . B .    . . . . .    . . . . .
. . . . .    . . . . .    . . W . . .    . W . . .    . W . . .    . W . . .
. W . .      . . W . .    . . W . .    . . . . .    . . . . .    . . P . .    . . P . .
. . P . .    . . P . .    . . P . .    . . P . .    . . P . .    . . . . .    . . . . .
```

This sequence is not actually self-contained. Black has alternative moves, but they only lead into other repeatable sequences in which white advances the pawn safely.

However, continual advancing of the pawn is not sufficient for White to win. Some repeatable patterns allow Black to choose stalemate when the pawn is on the 7th rank. These must be excluded from a set intended to identify wins.

By an initializing sequence we mean a sequence of moves by the kings only, that does not repeat, but which leads into a winning repetitive sequence. For example:

```
. . . . . B    . . . . . B    . . . . . .    . . . . . .    . . . . . .
. . . . . .    . . . . . .    . . . . B .    . . . . B .    . . . B . .
. . . . . .    . . . . . .    . . . . . .    . . . . . .    . . . . . .
. . . . . .    . . . . . .    . . . . . .    . . W . . .    . . W . . .
. . P . .      . W . P . .    . W . P . .    . . . P . .    . . . P . .
W . . . .      . . . . . .    . . . . . .    . . . . . .    . . . . . .
```

after which White can begin the repetitive sequence above.

The algorithm consists of three parts: (2) a set of basic patterns with known values; (b) a set of king-distance conditions extending some of the basic patterns; (c) the exhaustive search. Basically: the patterns recognize simple cases and the starting points of winning repetitive sequences; the king-distance conditions recognize some positions requiring an initializing sequence; and the exhaustive search finds values for positions not matched directly. All patterns assume White to play. At all Black-to-play positions, therefore, one ply of exhaustive search is required.

N.B. (a) 'Pattern' is used here to mean some specified relationship between the pieces, not necessarily by means of a diagram. (b) The pawn is always assumed to be white, playing up the board, and on the queen's side. (The pawn can never change files, so Q-side positions can be analysed independently of K-side positions. K-side positions are equivalent to their mirror images on the Q-side. Positions with a black pawn are equivalent to positions with colours and player's sides reversed.)

THE BASIC PATTERNS WITH KNOWN VALUES
(White-to-play positions only)
1. Stalemate.
2. Pawn captured.
3. Pawn-can-run. A position matches this pattern if:
    B rank < P rank *or* |B file − P file| > (8 − P rank)
4. Two repeatable patterns:
    1) `w .` or `. w` P not on R file;
       `. .`   `. .`   B anywhere
       `. P`   `P .`

    2) `* .` or `. *` P not on R file;
       `. .`   `. .`   B anywhere, except * if P rank ⩽ 4
       `w .`   `. w`
       `. P`   `P .`
5. Two non-repeatable patterns:
    1) `. B` or `B .` P not on R file;
       `. .`   `. .`   P rank = 6
       `w P`   `P w`

    2) `B . .` or `. . B` P not on R file;
       `. . .`   `. . .`   P rank = 5
       `w . P`   `P . w`

The pawn-can-run pattern is a version of the simple 'black king out-side the square of the pawn' rule given in elementary chess books.

Bramer (1977a) published an algorithm that recognizes every pawn-can-run position and which was verified to be correct, but it is quite complex and we wanted to keep our patterns and program structure as simple as possible. Most pawn-can-run positions not recognized by the simple rule can also be won, although requiring more moves, by king manoeuvring leading to a winning pattern that we do include.

The two repeatable patterns are the basis for recognizing the bulk of the remaining wins. The two non-repeatable patterns recognize a few extra positions where White's win does not pass through the other patterns.

The stalemate and pawn-captured patterns are draws by definition. A proof that the other patterns are wins appears in appendix 2. Essentially, the method is simply to examine the move tree from a given pattern establishing that White can reach some already-known winning pattern no matter what moves Black plays. However, unlike examining a move tree from an actual position, consideration must be given to whether each move from a particular pattern will be possible and legal in every position that corresponds to the pattern, and the analysis split into separate cases if not.

THE KING-DISTANCE CONDITIONS
AND THE EXHAUSTIVE SEARCH

The algorithm searches the move tree to evaluate a position, with positions matching a known pattern being terminal. In general, the more comprehensive the set of known patterns, the smaller such a search will be: yet it is desirable to keep the patterns few and simple to facilitate proof of correctness and in the interests of economy.

A good solution is to extend three of the basic patterns by king-distance conditions. These recognize many positions where one king is too far away from important squares to stop the other one establishing a known pattern by reaching a key square. For example, the position at the start of the initializing sequence given earlier matches basic pattern 2 via distance condition 2 and is therefore directly recognized as a win.

The first two conditions are sufficient for W to be sure of reaching repeatable patterns 1 and 2 respectively, and therefore identify wins.

The third condition is derived from the pawn-captured pattern and identifies draws.

The king-distance conditions are given in full, and proved correct, in appendix 3.

ALGORITHM PERFORMANCE

The algorithm is compact to code and the pattern matching can be executed very quickly. The overall speed of execution is proportional to the average number of lookahead positions in the exhaustive search. Whilst little or no search is needed for large classes of positions ranging from trivial to difficult, excessive search is needed for some others. This is due to two omissions from the algorithm as it stands: (a) the pawn was assumed not to be on the rook's file, and the double pawn advance was ignored; (b) too few patterns recognize draws, leaving most drawn positions to be evaluated by lookahead.

The first omission was deliberate, to simplify matters while starting this work. The second is perhaps more serious. It results from an early aim of detecting all wins by patterns, intending the algorithm to be entirely 'static' with no lookahead. Draws could then be identified indirectly by not matching any winning pattern. Having given up or at least postponed the aim of an entirely static algorithm, we now think repeatable drawing patterns as well as winning ones should have been included.

An additional winning pattern for the rook's file cases, one or two repeatable drawing patterns, and associated king-distance conditions will be required to rectify these omissions. On the other hand, the two non-repeatable winning patterns currently included could perhaps be discarded, as they recognize only eleven positions and these require little lookahead to detect the win.

We expect that the modified algorithm will then be fast overall, evaluating most positions without search.

CONCLUSIONS

This work has demonstrated that it is possible to create an efficient KPK algorithm that uses only simple, easily defined patterns, and which can be proved correct from its structure.

This is not to say that the algorithm was simple to devise. No chess book that we know gives information which is as complete; and the missing information is not only detail but concepts that each human has to learn (by means not understood) from the examples. Worse, humans who have learnt an adequate set of concepts from examples seem to find it very difficult, if not impossible, to define those concepts afterwards.

FUTURE WORK

The first step is to make the changes outlined in the discussion of algorithm performance. Our main interest is then to what extent the manual effort of creating the algorithm can be replaced by programmed activity.

The largest effort is in verifying pattern correctness by analysis of the move tree in pattern space, and this is apparently well suited to automation. A major difficulty though, as noted in appendix 2, is detecting when the analysis must be split into separate cases because a critical move is legal in some positions corresponding to the pattern but not in others. Moreover, splitting the analysis means dividing the original pattern into two separate patterns and there may be a choice of ways to do it. This choice may involve similar considerations to the original choice of what kind of pattern to use. Thus, move analysis in pattern space may not be straightforward. However, the attempt to program it should illuminate the goal of automatically generating suitable patterns.

Appendix 2. Analysis of the Basic Patterns

The analysis consists of examining the move tree derived from a pattern, nodes in the tree representing patterns rather than individual positions. Patterns with already known values are terminal nodes in the tree. In the case of 'repeatable' patterns, if a result is established for the pattern with the pawn on a particular rank, then, in the analysis of the pattern with the pawn on a lesser rank, a recurrence of the pattern with the pawn further advanced may be assigned the same value. In the case of two repeatable patterns, each of which leads into the other, the rank-7 result can be assumed, provided that a pawn advance is included in every cycle.

Two patterns are initially assumed to be terminal node wins:
1. P on rank 7: B not on or adjacent to queening square; White to play
   (In two positions, W needs to promote to R to avoid stalemate)
2. P on rank 7; W adjacent to queening square; White to play

Analysing patterns instead of individual positions introduces additional complexities. In particular, the analysis must be split into separate cases whenever it would otherwise contain a node at which the value is not the same for all positions that correspond to the pattern. This problem occurs when a critical move (or moves) is legal in some positions corresponding to the pattern but not in others.

The reasoning necessary to detect these cases and split the pattern appropriately is only given for the analysis of repeatable pattern 1: it probably would be the most difficult part of programming this kind of analysis. Also, the reasoning necessary to deduce what pattern exists after moves are made is only illustrated in the analysis of the pawn-can-run pattern. However, in the case of 'diagram-type' patterns, this reasoning is fairly straightforward.

THE PAWN-CAN-RUN PATTERN

B rank < P rank *or* |B file − P file| > (8 − P rank)

Case (a): White king not in front of the pawn on the same file

This case is analysed, rather than just assumed to be an elementary win, as it demonstrates that the verification can be treated as a search in the pattern tree.

Case (a.1): Pawn on rank 7
         = terminal pattern 1 : win

Case (a.2): Pawn rank ≤ 6

Analysis tree: Advance P, B any
    = pawn-can-run pattern (with P further advanced) : win
    Justification (a program to search move trees using patterns of this kind needs to make these deductions): The pawn advance must be legal (in all positions matching the pattern) since W is stated to be not in front and B cannot be while the pawn-can-run pattern is satisfied. After the pawn advance, the pawn rank is then 1 more, and as any B move can change rank and file by 1 at most, each inequality in the pawn-can-run pattern will still be true after B's reply if it is true before P's advance. Since one of them is true initially, the new node is also a pawn-can-run pattern.

Case (b): White king in front of P on the same file (P not on R file)

Case (b.1): White king immediately in front of the pawn; i.e.   . w +
Analysis tree: W plays to +, B any   . P .
    = repeatable pattern 2 : win
(The analysis of repeatable pattern 2 does not depend on case b of the pawn-can-run pattern.)
    Justification: W's move is legal since B cannot be adjacent to + while the pawn-can-run pattern is true. Nor can B be adjacent to * in repeatable pattern 2 for the same reason.

Case (b.2): White king not immediately in front of the pawn.
Analysis tree: P advance, B any
    = either pattern (b.1) : win
    or pattern (b.2) again with P advanced : win

REPEATABLE PATTERN 1

    w . or . w   P not on R file
    . .   . .   B anywhere
    . P   P .

Case (a): ‾‾‾ or ‾‾‾   (with P rank = 6 : the horizontal bar
            w .   . w   represents the top edge of the board)
            . .   . .
            . P   P .

Analysis tree: Advance P, B any
    = terminal pattern 2 : win

Case (b): ┌ B . .   sq. identification   ┌ a b c
             | . . W | d e f
             | . . . | g h i
             | . P .

Analysis tree: W to h, B to b, W to g, if B to a, advance P, B to b
    = non-repeatable pattern 1 : win
        if B other, W to d, B any
    = case (f) of repeatable pattern 1 : win

Case (c):　B * . . or . . * B
　　　　　. . + /　　/ + . .
　　　　　. W . .　　. . W .
　　　　　. . . .　　. . . .
　　　　　. . P .　　. P . .
Analysis tree: W to +, B any, advance P, B any, W to /, B any
　　　　　　　= repeatable pattern 1 (with P further advanced) : win

Case (d):　* B . or . B *
　　　　　÷ . /　　/ . ÷
　　　　　W + .　　. + W
　　　　　. . .　　. . .
　　　　　. P .　　. P .
Analysis tree: W to +, if B to *, W to /, B any, advance P, B any
　　　　　　　= repeatable pattern 1 (with P further advanced) : win
　　　　　　　　　if B other, W to ÷, B any, advance P, B any
　　　　　　　= repeatable pattern 1 (with P further advanced) : win

Case (e):　B B B or B B B
　　　　　. * .　　. * .
　　　　　. . .　　. . .
　　　　　. W .　　. W .
　　　　　. . .　　. . .
　　　　　. . P　　P . .
Analysis tree: Advance W, B any, advance P, B any
　　　　　　　= repeatable pattern 1 (with P advanced) : win

Case (f): Repeatable pattern 1, except cases (a-e)
Analysis tree: Advance P, B any
　　　　　　　= repeatable pattern 2 (with P advanced) : win

　　Justification for splitting into those cases (this reasoning must be performed by a program to search move trees in pattern space): Case (a) is
the highest possible pawn rank. It is examined first so that subsequent
analysis can take advantage of the repeating pattern. Cases (b-e) are separated from case (f) by starting with repeatable pattern 1 pretending that B
is not on the board. The following analysis tree can then be obtained:
　　　　　Advance P, — — —
　　　　　= repeatable pattern 2 (with P advanced) : win
　　In general, there are only four ways in which the black king's presence
can invalidate black-king-less analysis: (a) Occupying a square that prevents
any white move by obstruction; (b) To be able to take the pawn after a
white move; (c) To be in stalemate after a white move; (d) If the final white
move creates repeatable pattern 2, to be able to occupy the square * after it.
　　When applied to the analysis tree above, case (b) and cases (c-e) combined are separated from the residual case (f).
　　Splitting of the combined pattern (c-e) occurs when the white moves
that are legal in all positions corresponding to the combined pattern
(solidly legal) fail to lead to a win. The other three white moves must then
be examined, and the patterns (c)-(e) result from dividing the combined
pattern into pieces, in each of which one of the three moves is solidly legal.

REPEATABLE PATTERN 2

```
* .  or  . *    B not on *, if P rank ≤ 4
. .      . .
W .      . W
. P      P .
```

Case (a): As above, with P rank = 7
= terminal pattern 2 : win

Case (b):
```
B * . .   or   . . * B
. . + /        / + . .
. W . .        . . W .
. . P .        . P . .
```
W to +, B any, W to /, B any
= repeatable pattern 1 : win

Case (c):
```
* B .   or   . B *
÷ . /        / . ÷
W + .        . + W
. P .        . P .
```
W to +, if B to *, W to /, B any
= repeatable pattern 1 : win
      if B other, W to ÷, B any
= repeatable pattern 1 : win

Case (d):
```
w . .   or   . . w
. P B        B P .
```
Advance P, B any, advance W, B any
= repeatable pattern 2 (with P advanced) : win

Case (e):
```
W . .   or   . . W
. P .        . P .
B B B        B B B
```
= case (a) of pawn-can-run pattern. : win

Case (f):
```
. B . .   sq id: a b c d   or   . . B .   sq id: d c b a
. . . .          e f g h             . . . .          h g f e
. W . .          i j k l             . . W .          l k j i
. . P .                              . P . .
```
Advance P, if B to a, W to g, B any, W to d, B any
= repeatable pattern 1 : win
         if B to c
= non-repeatable pattern 1 : win

Case (g): Repeatable pattern 2, except cases (b)-(f)
Advance W, B any
= repeatable pattern 1 : win

Non-Repeatable Pattern 1

```
. B  or  B .    P not on R file
. .      . .    P rank = 6
W P      P W
```

Case (a):
```
. B .
+ . *
W P .
```
Analysis tree: Advance P, B to *, W to +, B any
        = terminal pattern 2 : win

Case (b): Reflection about the pawn of case a

Non-Repeatable Pattern 2

```
B . .  or  . . B    P not on R file
. . .      . . .    P rank = 5
W . P      P . W
```

Case (a):
```
. . . .   sq. identification    a b c d
. . B .                         e f g h
. . . .                         i j k l
P . W .                         P . W .
```

Analysis tree: Advance P, if B to b, W to j(=z), if B to a
        = non-repeatable pattern 1 : win
                if B to c, advance P, B any
        = terminal pattern 1 : win
            if B to c, W to k, if B to b, W to j
        = pattern z : win
                if B to d, advance P, B any
        = terminal pattern 1 : win
            if B other, advance P, B any
        = terminal pattern 1 : win

Case (b):
```
. . . .   Reflection about the pawn of case a
. B . .
. . . .
. W . P
```

Case (c):
```
. . . .   sq. identification   a b c d
B . . .                        e f g h
. . . .                        i j k l
W . P .
```

Analysis tree: Advance P, if B to b, W to j(=y), if B to c
        = non-repeatable pattern 1 : win
                if B to a, W to g, B to e,
                W to h, B any,
                advance P, B any
        = terminal pattern 2 : win
            if B to a, W to i, B to b, W to j
        = pattern y : win

Appendix 3. Initialising King-Move Sequences

Some classes of KPK positions seem to be 'simple' to value because one king is 'clearly too far away' to stop the other achieving its goals. The king-distance conditions derived below make this notion precise enough to define patterns and prove them correct.

The first step is to derive conditions for one king to reach a particular square despite interference from the other king. Conditions for reaching a given pattern can then be deduced. A decision cannot always be reached on the basis of distance alone. If the distances are nearly the same and the kings are either close or might become so, their ability to block each other's squares could favour either one, depending on the precise position. However, if B → S is sufficiently less than W → S, or sufficiently greater, an immediate decision is possible.

Exact conditions for such decisions can be established with the aid of two measures of distance.

1. 'geometric' distance (gdist) = max(file difference, rank diff)

2. 'K-move' distance (kdist) = the number of king moves needed to reach the target square taking squares blocked by the pawn into account, but not squares blocked or potentially blockable by the other king.

N.B. gdist always ⩽ kdist for either king.

There are two cases:

1. A sufficient condition that W (the king on move) can reach T despite any move by B is: $\mathrm{kdist}(W,T) > \mathrm{gdist}(B,T)$.

2. A sufficient condition that B (not on move) can reach T, and, as a corollary, that W cannot, is: $\mathrm{gdist}(W,T) > \mathrm{kdist}(B,T)+1$.

It is possible to convince oneself of the truth of these conditions by informal reasoning, but a formal proof by induction offers greater protection against oversights:

Case 1: Let $\mathrm{kdist}(W,T) = n$

a) If $n = 0$ then true since W on T already.

b) Suppose true for some n. Consider any square R for which $\mathrm{kdist}(R,T) = n+1$, and any square for B such that $\mathrm{gdist}(B,T) > n+1$. R must be adjacent to some square S for which $\mathrm{kdist}(S,T) = n$. B cannot be adjacent to S since then $\mathrm{gdist}(S,T) \leqslant n$ which would imply $\mathrm{gdist}(B,T) \leqslant n+1$. Therefore B does not prevent W moving to S.[1] After B's reply to W's move to S, $\mathrm{gdist}(B,T)$ must still be at least $n+1$ which is $> \mathrm{kdist}(S,T)$. By the induction hypothesis W can then reach T. Therefore true for n implies true for $n+1$.

[1] This reasoning step would not be valid if Black's distance were calculated taking squares blocked by the pawn into account, since B might be adjacent to S but have dist >1 because it was unable to move there. E.g. . . w On
. S .
B . P

Case 2:

a) True if kdist(B,T) = 0, since B already on T.

b) For kdist(B,T) = n, consider any square for W for which gdist(W,T) > n+1. After W's first move to any square S, gdist(S,T) > n. I.e. kdist(B,T) < gdist(S,T). Then by reversal of colours, case 1 implies that B can reach T.

From these single-square reachability conditions, king-distance conditions ensuring the reachability of repeatable patterns 1 and 2 may be deduced:

1. Let T = (either) square W in repeatable pattern 1. If kdist(W,T) < gdist(B,T) then W can reach its 'key' square in repeatable pattern 1. The only two ways this can fail to actually achieve the pattern are: (a) if Black can take the pawn before W reaches its key square, and (b) if Black is stalemated. Kdist(B,P) > kdist(W,T) guarantees that Black cannot take the pawn in the time that W needs to reach T. P rank < 6 guarantees that no stalemate is possible since all the stalemate positions have P rank = 6 or 7. Therefore

> kdist(W,T) < gdist(B,T) *and*
> kdist(B,P) > kdist(W,T) *and*
> P rank < 6   implies White can win.

2. Let T = (either) square W in repeatable pattern 2. If kdist(W,T) < gdist(B,T) then W can reach its key square. If kdist(B,*) > kdist(W,T) then B cannot defend by reaching *. If kdist(B,P) > kdist(W,T) −1 then black cannot capture the pawn (it must be done in 1 move less than kdist(W,T) since T is adjacent to P). If P rank < 6 no stalemate positions can occur. Therefore

> kdist(W,T) < gdist(B,T) *and*
> kdist(B,*) > kdist(W,T) *and*
> kdist(B,P) > kdist(W,T) −1 *and*
> P rank < 6   implies W has a win

The single-square reachability conditions are only valid while P does not move. Every time P moves, kdist has to be redefined. This subtlety did not arise in the above king-distance conditions because they define positions in which white can reach a known win by king moves alone. The next king-distance condition defines positions in which B can reach P despite the efforts of W. Although primarily concerned with king moves, the analysis must also consider P moves. Rather than attempt to redefine single-square reachability, a direct proof by induction is given.

3. 'B rank ⩾ P rank *and* gdist(W,P) > kdist(B,P)+1 implies draw.' Let kdist(B,P) = n.

a) True if n = 0. B has just taken P.

b) Suppose true for n. Consider any square for B for which kdist(B,P) = n + 1, and any square for W such that gdist(W,P) > n + 2. We now seek to prove that, after any white move, B has a reply that creates the kdist(B,P) = n case.

---

the other hand, if White's distance did not take blocked squares into account, W might be adjacent to S, but unable to go there.

Neither a W or a P move (the double pawn advance is ignored) can reduce gdist(W,P) by more than 1, and kdist(B,P) = n + 1 implies that B has a move to a square S such that kdist(S,P) = n. So it is sufficient to show that W does not obstruct B to S after any W move and that kdist(B,P) is still $\leqslant n$ + 1 after a P move.

(a) A W move to any square R: gdist(W,P) $>$ n + 2 implies gdist(R,P) $>$ n + 1. R cannot be adjacent to S since as kdist(S,P) = n, gdist(S,P) $\leqslant n$ and therefore gdist(R,P) would be $\leqslant n$ + 1.

(b) A P advance: Consider the geometry of the squares that P blocks from B. Let kd = kdist(B,P) and gd = gdist(B,P).

i) kd is either gd or gd + 1.
Hence, if kd after the P advance is to be $>$ kd before, kd before = gd and kd after = gd + 1.

ii) If kd = gd + 1, B must be diagonally in front of P.
Hence, by geometry, if kd before = gd and kd after = gd + 1, gd after = gd before $-$ 1.

iii) The P advance cannot increase gd as B rank $\geqslant$ p rank.
Therefore kdist(B,P before) $\leqslant$ kdist(B,P after).
Hence true for n implies true for n + 1.

SUMMARY OF KING-DISTANCE CONDITIONS
(applicable to white-to-play positions only)
1. Win if: kdist(W,W1) $<$ gdist(B,W1) *and*
    kdist(B,P) $>$ kdist(W,W1) *and*
    P rank $<$ 6
2. Win if: kdist(W,W2) $<$ gdist(B,W2) *and*
    kdist(B,S) $>$ kdist(W,W2) *and*
    kdist(B,P) $>$ kdist(W,W2) $-$ 1 *and*
    P rank $<$ 6
3. Draw if: kdist(B,P) $<$ gdist(W,P) $-$ 1 *and*
    B rank $\geqslant$ P rank

W, B and P denote the squares occupied by the white king, black king and white pawn in the position under consideration. W1 and W2 are the squares W in repeatable patterns 1 and 2, when aligned so that P in the pattern coincides with P in the position. S is the square * in repeatable pattern 2.

Appendix 4. The Difficulty of Backing Up

The first examples are based on the least ambitious description scheme we could devise. Each description gives the rank of each piece, but gives the files of the kings relative to the pawn, instead of absolutely. The file of the pawn is not specified, thus each description covers up to four positions. This choice originated from the observation that many patterns of pieces were consistently wins or losses irrespective of which file the pawn was on. We called these descriptions VPF (for Variable Pawn File) patterns.

Some VPF patterns have four positions corresponding to them (one for each possible file for the pawn), e.g: w . в   Call these 's-patterns'.
                                                                   p . .

Others have only one to three e.g: в . w Call these 'd-patterns'.
                                   . . p

Patterns adjacent to d-patterns are a problem, because they may have a move (to the d-pattern) which is legal in some occurrences of the pattern and not others. If this move is critical (e.g. the only legal move) then the pattern may not have a common value over all its occurrences. For example:

в .   Black to play, is adjacent to в . .   which is a d-pattern
p .   . p .
. w   . . w

The former pattern, an s-pattern, is a loss with P on Q-file, B-file or N-file, but a draw with P on R-file.

Consequently, in the systematic valuing process ('backing up'), after valuing a pattern with multiple values, any VPF pattern adjacent to it may in turn have multiple value, and therefore must be processed position by position instead of as a pattern. Thus any VPF pattern adjacent to either a d-pattern or to a multiple-valued pattern must be processed as individual positions instead of as a pattern.[1] Unfortunately, this includes most VPF patterns. Moreover, as a practical exercise in programming, the slight reduction in computation from the few VPF patterns that can be processed as entities is swamped by the overheads of handling patterns as well as positions.

The remaining examples illustrate the difficulties of manipulating more elaborate descriptions. They are based on a description scheme we called distance-based patterns. Each description consists of a logical combination (ands, ors and nots) of predicates. Each predicate expresses a distance relation (=, > or <) either between squares, or between ranks and files.

[1]This might not be the case if suitable 'frame axioms' about the relationship of various moves to possible changes in values could be found, but this seems very difficult indeed.

Systematic valuing by backing up requires:

1. Generating descriptions one ply back (i.e. generating a description matching a set of positions such that each is one ply back from some position matching the starting description).

2. Generating and examining descriptions 1 ply forward again from the one ply back description (this will include the original description amongst others) to establish a minimax value for the backed up description if possible.

Unfortunately, this cannot be done by simple cycling through a small set of well-defined possibilities as in position space.

Unlike position space and VPF-pattern space, descriptions are neither necessarily unique nor distinct. Also, it is not usually appropriate or feasible to divide up positions one ply distant into eight descriptions corresponding to the different directions of king moves.

Moreover, only descriptions with consistent values are useful (by consistent is meant that all positions matching the description have the same minimax value), and some means has to be found to restrict the generation of descriptions to consistent ones or detect and divide up inconsistent ones.

These problems can best be illustrated with an example. A description of White 1-ply wins is:

WTP & PR = 7 & W → Q = 1 (White to play, pawn rank = 7 and
dist(white king, queening square) = 1)

or WTP & PR = 7 & B → Q > 1 & W → Q > 0

Generating a description of Black 2-ply losses might proceed by generating first a description of losses 1-ply back from the component 1 (PR = 7 & W → Q = 1) of the White 1-ply wins and then component 2.

The first of these is actually feasible with this description and might go as follows:

B moves cannot affect this description component except for changing the side to play and so any position matching BTP & PR = 7 & W → Q = 1 is a position one black ply back. Each of these will be a loss if and only if all WTP positions one black ply forward are White wins. All Black moves lead straight back into the original description and so 'BTP & PR = 7 & W → Q = 1' are indeed 2-ply losses.

However, the second description component is a different matter. One set of positions one black ply backwards is obtained by changing B → Q > 1 into B → Q > 2. This set can be deduced to be consistent and a 2-ply loss for Black, since any black forward move still leaves B → Q > 1. The remainder of the positions one black ply back provides all the difficulty.

Another set of positions one black ply back is 'BTP & PR = 7 & B → Q = 1 & W → Q > 0'. This set is not consistent valued and it does not seem feasible to divide it into consistent subsets by reasoning about distances, or indeed by any process of reasoning sufficiently well-defined to program. The positions may be diagrammed:

```
. B . . . B .   W anywhere except in front of P, horizontal line
. B . P . B .   indicates edge of board
. B B B B B .
. . . . . . .
```

Of these, by hand examination, the following positions are losses:

(1)
```
. . B
P . B
W . B
```
(2)
```
. . B
P . .
. W W
```
(3)
```
. W W
P . .
. . B
```

(4)
```
B . .
B . P
B . W
```
(5)
```
B . .   P not on B-file
. . P
W W .
```
(6)
```
W W .
. . P
B . .
```

These may be described using distances by:

BTP & PR = 7 & W → Q > 0 & B → Q = 2 & W → * = 1 & B → * = 1 &
B → P > 1 where * = square to right of pawn

and

BTP & PR = 7 & W → Q > 0 & B → Q = 2 & W → $ = 1 & B → $ = 1 &
B → P > 1 & B → A8 > 0 where $ = square to left of pawn, and
A8 = 8th rank on rook's file

Further positions one black ply back are obtained with B → Q = 1, but after hand examination none are Black 2-ply losses.

But these descriptions were generated *ad hoc* as the need for them arose. No systematic deductive method of obtaining them is apparent.

Going further back the descriptions required to generate consistent subsets become more complicated still, essentially for reasons similar to those above. In general the requirement of consistency appears to lead to an unavoidable proliferation of predicates.

Appendix 5. Discriminating Wins from Draws in KPK

A FORTRAN subroutine that determines, for any chess position with just king and one pawn versus king, whether it is a win or a draw has been developed while investigating aspects of KPK. White-to-play positions are evaluated directly, by a series of tests on the ranks and files of the pieces. Black-to-play positions are evaluated by a 1-ply lookahead. The subroutine has been tested against a complete table of KPK values (Clarke 1977) and is correct in all cases.

The tests applied to White-to-play positions are mostly based on geometric distances (max(filedist, rankdist)) between various pieces and squares. Some combinations imply a win for White, others, a draw. No claim is made that the tests are the most economical possible – on the contrary there probably is a great deal of room for improvement, as simply achieving any complete set was the goal.

This work grew out of current SRC-supported research into description generation and deduction in king and pawn endings. While studying the properties of geometric distances as a possible basis for position descriptions that might be suitable for mechanical generation, it was appropriate to see how convenient such descriptions were for classifying KPK positions, regardless of how the descriptions might be obtained. It was not necessary to create the subroutine described here for this purpose but having got part way surprisingly quickly it seemed worthwhile to finish it for another reason. Namely, that although KPK information has been programmed by several researchers (Bramer 1977, Harris 1977, Piasetski 1977, Tan 1972) and other chess endgame information by (Bramer 1975, Huberman 1968, Michie 1977, Newborn 1977, Tan 1973, 1974 & 1977, Zuidema 1974), no KPK program has yet been written that is known to be correct in all cases. Consequently, such a program might be useful for comparison and reference.

No attempt was made to keep to 'mechanizable' descriptions when extending the classification rules to be correct on all KPK positions. The technique used was to systematically compare the current routine with the complete KPK table until several misclassifications had been accumulated, then study them and devise new or modified rules which resulted in correct classification for the wrong ones plus as many other cases as could be intuitively generalized from these examples. The modified routine was then tested, etc.

The feedback from the perfect information in the complete KPK table resulted in very quick (about two weeks) development of the routine. This is perhaps the most important point presented here. Other workers have

```
      FUNCTION  KPKWV(PF,PR,WF,WR,BF,BR)
      INTEGER  PF,PR,WF,WR,BF,BR,DIST
      INTEGER  PPR,BQ,BPP,WPP,BRPU,BRPUUU
      INTEGER  BLPU,BLPUU,BLPUUU,WRPU,WRPUU,WLPU
      INTEGER  WLPUU,WBDD,SGF,SGR,WSG,SDR,WSD,BSD,TBF
      KPKWV=1
      PPR=PR
      IF(PR.EQ.2)  PPR=3
      IF(PF.NE.1)  GOTO 2
      IF(BF.NE.3)  GOTO 1
      IF(PR.EQ.7.AND.WF.EQ.1.AND.WR.EQ.8.AND.BR.GT.6)  GOTO 98
      IF(PR.EQ.6.AND.WF.LT.4.AND.WR.EQ.6.AND.BR.EQ.8)  GOTO 99
1     IF(BF.EQ.1.AND.BR.GT.PR)  GOTO 98
      IF(PR.EQ.7.AND.BF.GT.2)  GOTO 99
      IF(BF.LE.3.AND.BR-PPR.GT.1)  GOTO 98
      IF(WF.EQ.1.AND.BF.EQ.3.AND.WR-PR.EQ.1.AND.BR-PR.EQ.1)  GOTO 98
2     BQ=DIST(BF,BR,PF,8)
      IF(BQ.GT.8-PPR)  GOTO 99
      MBPF=BF-PF
      IF(MBPF.LT.0)  MBPF=-MBPF
      BPP=DIST(BF,BR,PF,PPR)
      WPP=DIST(WF,WR,PF,PPR)
      IF(BPP-WPP.LT.-1.AND.BR-PR.NE.MBPF)  GOTO 98
      IF(PF.EQ.1.AND.PR.LE.3.AND.WF.LE.2.AND.WR.EQ.8
1     .AND.BF.EQ.4.AND.BR.GE.7)  GOTO 99
      IF(PF.NE.2.OR.PR.NE.6.OR.BF.NE.1.OR.BR.NE.8)  GOTO 3
      IF(WF.LE.3.AND.WR.EQ.6)  GOTO 98
      IF(WF.EQ.4.AND.WR.EQ.8)  GOTO 98
3     IF(PR.NE.7)  GOTO 4
      IF(WR.LT.8.AND.WPP.EQ.2.AND.BQ.EQ.0)  GOTO 99
      IF(WR.EQ.6.AND.WF.EQ.PF.AND.BQ.EQ.0)  GOTO 99
      IF(WR.GE.6.AND.WPP.LE.2.AND.BQ.NE.0)  GOTO 99
4     BLPUU=DIST(BF,BR,PF-1,PR+2)
      WBDD=DIST(WF,WR,BF,BR-2)
      BRPUU=DIST(BF,BR,PF+1,PR+2)
      IF(PR.NE.6)  GOTO 6
      IF(DIST(BF,BR,PF+1,PR).GT.1.AND.
1     BRPUU.GT.DIST(WF,WR,PF+1,PR))  GOTO 99
      IF(PF.EQ.1)  GOTO 5
      IF(BLPUU.GT.DIST(WF,WR,PF-1,PR))  GOTO 99
      IF(BR.EQ.8.AND.MBPF.EQ.1.AND.WBDD.EQ.1)  GOTO 99
      IF(BR.GT.6.AND.MBPF.EQ.2.AND.DIST(WF,WR,BF,5).LE.1)  GOTO 99
      GOTO 6
5     IF(WF.EQ.1.AND.WR.EQ.8.AND.BF.EQ.2.AND.BR.EQ.6)  GOTO 98
6     MWPF=WF-PF
      IF(MWPF.LT.0)  MWPF=-MWPF
      IF(PR.GE.5.AND.MWPF.EQ.2.AND.WR.EQ.PR.AND.BF.EQ.WF
1     .AND.BR-PR.EQ.2)  GOTO 99
      BRPU=DIST(BF,BR,PF+1,PR+1)
      WRPU=DIST(WF,WR,PF+1,PR+1)
      BLPU=DIST(BF,BR,PF-1,PR+1)
      WLPU=DIST(WF,WR,PF-1,PR+1)
      IF(PF.EQ.1.OR.PR.NE.5)  GOTO 7
      IF(MWPF.LE.1.AND.WR-PR.EQ.1)  GOTO 99
      IF(WRPU.EQ.1.AND.BRPU.GT.1)  GOTO 99
      IF(WR.GE.4.AND.BF.EQ.WF.AND.BR-PR.GE.2.AND.MBPF.EQ.3)  GOTO 99
      IF(WLPU.EQ.1.AND.BLPU.GT.1)  GOTO 99
7     IF(PR.EQ.2.AND.BR.EQ.3.AND.MBPF.GT.1.AND.
1     DIST(WF,WR,BF,BR+2).LE.1)  GOTO 99
```

Figure 1

```
      IF(WR-PR.EQ.2.AND.BR.EQ.PR.AND.MBPF.EQ.1.AND.MWPF.GT.1
     1   .AND.(WF-PF)*(BF-PF).GT.0)  GOTO 98
      IF(PF.EQ.1.AND.WF.EQ.1.AND.WR.EQ.BR.AND.BF.GT.3)  GOTO 99
      SGF=PF-1
      IF(WF.GE.PF)  SGF=PF+1
      SGR=WR-(MWPF-1)
      IF(MWPF.EQ.0.AND.WR.GT.BR)  SGR=WR-1
      WSG=DIST(WF,WR,SGF,SGR)
      IF(WR-PR-MWPF.GT.0.AND.WR-BR.GE.-1.AND.BPP-(WSG+(SGR-PPR))
     1   .GE.-1.AND.DIST(BF,BR,SGF,SGR).GT.WSG)  GOTO 99
      MD=MBPF-MWPF
      IF(PF.NE.1.OR.BF.LE.3)  GOTO 8
      SDR=BR+(BF-3)
      IF(SDR.GT.8)  SDR=8
      IF(WR.GT.BR+1)  SDR=BR
      IF(SDR.LE.PPR)  GOTO 8
      WSD=DIST(WF,WR,3,SDR)
      BSD=DIST(BF,BR,3,SDR)
      IF(BSD-WSD.LT.-1)  GOTO 98
      IF(BSD.LE.WSD.AND.MD.LE.0)  GOTO 98
   8  BRPUUU=DIST(BF,BR,PF+1,PR+3)
      IF(BRPU.GT.WRPU.AND.BRPUUU.GT.WRPU.AND.PR-WR.NE.PF-WF)
     1   GOTO 99
      IF(BRPUUU.EQ.0.AND.WRPU.EQ.1)  GOTO 99
      BLPUUU=DIST(BF,BR,PF-1,PR+3)
      IF(PF.EQ.1)  GOTO 9
      IF(BLPU.GT.WLPU.AND.BLPUUU.GT.WLPU.AND.PR-WR.NE.WF-PF)
     1   GOTO 99
      IF(BLPUUU.EQ.0.AND.WLPU.EQ.1)  GOTO 99
   9  WRPUU=DIST(WF,WR,PF+1,PR+2)
      IF(BRPUU.GT.WRPUU)  GOTO 99
      WLPUU=DIST(WF,WR,PF-1,PR+2)
      IF(PF.GT.1.AND.BLPUU.GT.WLPUU)  GOTO 99
      IF(BR.NE.PR)  GOTO 10
      IF(MWPF.LE.2.AND.WR-PR.EQ.-1.AND.MBPF.NE.2)  GOTO 99
      IF(DIST(WF,WR,BF-1,BR+2).LE.1.AND.BF-PF.GT.1)  GOTO 99
      IF(DIST(WF,WR,BF+1,BR+2).LE.1.AND.BF-PF.LT.-1)  GOTO 99
  10  IF(PF.EQ.1)  GOTO 11
      IF(BR.EQ.PR.AND.MBPF.GT.1.AND.
     1   DIST(WF,WR,PF,PR-1).LE.1)  GOTO 99
      IF(BR-PR.GE.3.AND.WBDD.EQ.1)  GOTO 99
      IF(WR-PR.EQ.2.AND.WR.LT.BR.AND.MD.GE.0)  GOTO 99
      IF(MWPF.LE.2.AND.WR-PR.GE.3.AND.BF.NE.PF
     1   .AND.WR-BR.LE.1)  GOTO 99
      IF(WR.GE.PR.AND.BR-PR.GE.5.AND.MBPF.GE.3
     1   .AND.MD.GE.-1.AND.PPR.EQ.3)  GOTO 99
      IF(MD.GE.-1.AND.PR.EQ.2.AND.BR.EQ.8)  GOTO 99
  11  TBF=BF-1
      IF(PF.GT.BF)  TBF=BF+1
      IF(MBPF.GT.1.AND.BR.EQ.PPR.AND.
     1   DIST(WF,WR,TBF,BR+2).LE.1)  GOTO 99
      IF(BR.EQ.PR.AND.BF-PF.EQ.-2.AND.
     1   DIST(WF,WR,PF+2,PR-1).LE.1)  GOTO 99
      IF(PF.GT.2.AND.BR.EQ.PR.AND.BF-PF.EQ.2.AND.
     1   DIST(WF,WR,PF-2,PR-1).LE.1)  GOTO 99
  98  KPKWV=0
  99  RETURN
      END
```

Figure 1 (continued)

```
FUNCTION  KPKBV (PF,PR,WF,WR,BF,BR)
INTEGER  PF,PR,WF,WR,BF,BR,INCF(8),INCR(8),DIST
DATA  INCF/0,1,1,1,0,-1,-1,-1/,INCR/1,1,0,-1,-1,-1,0,1/
KPKBV=0
NM=0
DO 1 I=1,8
NBF=BF+INCF(I)
IF(NBF.LT.1.OR.NBF.GT.8)  GOTO 1
NBR=BR+INCR(I)
IF(NBR.LT.1.OR.NBR.GT.8)  GOTO 1
IF(DIST(NBF,NBR,WF,WR).LT.2)  GOTO 1
IF(NBF.EQ.PF.AND.NBR.EQ.PR)  GOTO 2
IF(NBR.EQ.PR+1.AND.(NBF.EQ.PF-1.OR.NBF.EQ.PF+1))  GOTO 1
NM=NM+1
IF(KPKWV(PF,PR,WF,WR,NBF,NBR).EQ.0)  GOTO 2
1  CONTINUE
IF(NM.GT.0)  KPKBV=-1
2  RETURN
END

INTEGER FUNCTION DIST(F1,R1,F2,R2)
INTEGER  F1,R1,F2,R2,FD,RD
FD=F2-F1
IF(FD.LT.0)  FD=-FD
RD=R2-R1
IF(RD.LT.0)  RD=-RD
DIST=FD
IF(RD.GT.DIST)  DIST=RD
RETURN
END
```

Figure 2

spent a great deal of time and effort transforming this kind of information into a computer program and it may be that a large portion of this effort lies in a possibly unsuspected quarter — that of being their own 'devil's advocate' when considering the correctness or otherwise of parts or proposed parts of their algorithm. I found it very much easier to suggest new classification rules (which might or might not be correct) than to test them for correctness. With a rapid-response machine to test each rule immediately and print exceptions and omissions the task of evolving a complete set became easy.

One noticeable phenomenon was that the number of tests increased disproportionately as fewer and fewer positions remained misclassified. This has been anticipated as inevitable for such tasks by Zuidema (Zuidema 1974) but it may have been due only to spending insufficient time on the task — when new rules were found to be necessary they were added without always examining existing rules to see if they were made redundant by the new rule or looking for ways to combine them into more economical rules. Greater chess expertise would probably have helped!

Figure 1 is a listing of the main routine, KPKWV, which yields a result of 1 if the position specified by PF (pawn file), PR (pawn rank), WF (white-king file), WR, BF, BR and with White to play is a win, 0 if it is a draw. Figure 2 lists the lookahead routine KPKBV that returns −1 if the configuration specified with black to play is a loss, 0 if a draw. Both routines

	1	2	3	4	5	6	7	8	9	10	11	12	13	14	15	16	17	18	19	20	21	22	2
	D	W	D	W	D	D	W	D	W	D	D	W	W	W	W	W	W	W	D	W	W	W	W
PF	=1	=1	=1	=1	=1	=1			=1	=2	=2					>1	>1	>1	=1		>1	>1	>
PR	=7	=6		=7					≤3	=6	=6	=7	=7	=7	=6	=6	=6	=6	=6	≥5	=5	=5	=
WF	=1	<4				=1			≤2	≤3	=4								=1				
WR	=8	=6							=8	=6	=8	<8	=6	≥6					=8				≥
BF	=3	=3	=1	>2	≤3	=3			=4	=1	=1								=2				
BR	>6	=8							≥7	=8	=8						=8	>6	=6				
WR-PR						=1														=0	=1		
BR-PR			>0			=1														=2			≥
WR-BR																							
BF-PF																							
|WF-PF|													=0							=2	≤1		
|BF-PF|																	=1	=2					=
BF-WF																				=0			=
					(BR-PPR)>1		(B→Q)>(PP→Q)	(B→PP)-(W→PP)<-1 & (BR-PR)≠|BF-PF|				(W→PP)=2 & (B→Q)=0	(B→Q)=0	(W→PP)≤2 & (B→Q)≠0	(B→[RP++])>(W→RP)&(B→RP)>1	(B→[LP++])>(W→LP)	(W→[B--])=1	(W→[BF,5])≤1				(W→[RP+])=1 & (B→[RP+])>1	

Figure 3

26	27	28	29	30	31	32	33	34	35	36	37	38	39	40	41	42	43	44	45	46	47	48	
D	W	W	D	D	W	W	W	W	W	W	W	W	W	W	W	W	W	W	W	W	W	W	
	$=1$		$=1$	$=1$		>1	>1		>1					>1	>1	>1	>1	>1	>1			>2	PF
																		$=2$					PR
		$=1$																					WF
																							WR
	>3		>3	>3																			BF
																		$=8$					BR
											$=-1$					$\geqslant 2$	$\geqslant 3$	$\geqslant 0$					WR-PR
$=0$											$=0$	$=0$	$=0$	$=0$	$\geqslant 3$			$\geqslant 5$			$=0$	$=0$	BR-PR
		$=0$	$\geqslant -1$													<0	$\leqslant 1$						WR-BR
												>1	<-1								$=-2$	$=2$	BF-PF
>1											$\leqslant 2$						$\leqslant 2$						$\lvert$WF-PF$\rvert$
$=1$											$\neq 2$			>1			$\neq 0$	$\geqslant 3$		>1			$\lvert$BF-PF$\rvert$
																							BF-WF

$(w \to [LLP-]) \leqslant 1$

$(w \to [RRP-]) \leqslant 1$

$BR = PPR \ \& \ (w \to [TB++]) \leqslant 1$

$\lvert BF-PF \rvert - \lvert WF-PF \rvert \geqslant -1$

$PPR = 3 \ \& \ \lvert BF-PF \rvert - \lvert WF-PF \rvert \geqslant -1$

$\lvert BF-PF \rvert \geqslant \lvert WF-PF \rvert$

$(w \to [B-\llcorner]) = 1$

$(w \to [P-\llcorner]) \leqslant 1$

$(w \to [RB++]) \leqslant 1$

$(w \to [LB++]) \leqslant 1$

$(B \to [LLP++]) > (w \to [LP++])$

$(B \to [RP++]) > (w \to [RP++])$

$(B \to [LP+++]) = 0 \ \& \ (w \to [LP+++])$

$(B \to [LP+++]) = 0 \ \& \ (w \to [LP+++])$

$(B \to [RP+++]) = 0 \ \& \ (w \to [RP+]) = 1$

$(B \to [RP+]) > (w \to [RP+]) \ \& \ (B \to [RP+++]) > (w \to [RP+]) \ \& \ (PR-WR) \neq (PF-WF)$

$(B \to [LP+]) > (w \to [LP+]) \ \& \ (B \to [LP+++]) > (w \to [LP+]) \ \& \ (PR-WR) \neq (WF-PF)$

$(B \to SD) < (w \to SD) \ \& \ SDR > PPR \ \& \ \lvert BF-PF \rvert \leqslant \lvert WF-PF \rvert$

$(B \to SD) < (w \to SD) \ \& \ SDR > PPR$

$(B \to SD) - (w \to SD) < -1 \ \& \ SDR > PPR$

$(B \to PP) - ((w \to SG) + (SGR-PPR)) \geqslant -1 \ \& \ (WR-PR) > \lvert WF-PF \rvert \ \& \ (B \to SG) > (w \to SG)$

$Sign(WF-PF) = Sign(BF-PF)$

```
P                  Square pawn is on
W                  Square white king is on
B                  Square black king is on
F                  File.  E.g. PF = file pawn is on
R (as suffix)      Rank.  E.g. WR = rank of white king
PP                 = P unless PR=2 when = square in front of pawn
Q                  Square on which pawn will queen.  I.e. QF=PF, QR=8
→                  Distance between squares.
                       E.g. W→P = max(|WF-PF|, |WR-PR|)
L                  Left side.  E.g. LP = square to left of pawn
R (as prefix)      Right side
+ (within [ ])     Up.  E.g. [P+] = square in front of pawn
- (within [ ])     Down
[ ]                Square.  E.g. [RP+] is the sq. diagonally in front of P
[f,r]              Square where f is the file and r the rank
T                  1 file towards pawn.
                       E.g. TBF = if BF > PF then BF-1 else BF+1
SD                 A square defined by:
                       SDF = 3; SDR = if WR ≤ BR+1 then BR+BF-3 else BR
SG                 A square defined by:
                       SGF = if WF < PF then PF-1 else PF+1
                       SGB = if WF=PF & WR>BR then WR-1 else WR-|WF-PF|+1
```

Files are numbered 1-8 from the queen's rook file to the king's
rook file; the queen's side is the left side; the ranks are
numbered 1-8 from White's side to Black's side; and the Black
side is up.

Figure 4. Key to non-standard notation

assume the pawn is white and that it is on the Queen's side of the board.
Values for the other KPK positions can be obtained by symmetry. The
pawn must not be on the 8th rank.

Figure 3 is a representation of the logic of the decision rules for
KPKWV which is partly a decision table and partly boolean expressions.
There are 48 rules (or tests), which are applied in sequence 1-48. If one
is found to be applicable it yields a value W or D (win or draw) and immediate exit from the routine. If no applicable rule is found the default is
draw. A rule is applicable if and only if every condition is met. In other
words, it is the logical 'and' of the conditions and there are no 'or'ed
conditions. This voluntary restriction facilitated recording the rules as a
decision table during development, which was convenient as it required
little writing, was easy to alter, and compact enough to enable the rules
to be viewed *en bloc*. The top half of the table gives some conditions in
decision-table form; the lower half contains those conditions that only
appear in one or two rules entered separately for each rule as a boolean
expression. Figure 4 is the key to the notation used.

Figure 5 lists the number of configurations recognized by each rule
but not by those preceeding it. N.B. The rules are not in chronological
order of generation as new rules and modifications were sometimes ac-
companied by shuffling the order — one reason being to put simple and
quick tests before more complex ones, another being to correct rules by
testing for exceptions beforehand.

A subroutine that plays KPK can readily be constructed using KPKWV
and KPKBV to provide the win/draw information. It is not quite enough,
however, to ensure that the move chosen is a win if one exists. The choice

1	2	11	1	21	216	31	3469	41	448
2	3	12	24	22	315	32	63	42	39
3	1344	13	3	23	40	33	2527	43	342
4	3070	14	237	24	234	34	36	44	117
5	1789	15	235	25	150	35	1531	45	12
6	5	16	303	26	24	36	840	46	2
7	54336	17	27	27	48	37	171	47	12
8	7374	18	54	28	4783	38	63	48	9
9	8	19	1	29	1155	39	9		
10	3	20	5	30	387	40	60		

Figure 5. Number of configurations detected by each rule

must ensure progress towards the win, as procrastination can lead to a draw by repetition or 50-move rule. This is easy for KPK, and I believe that the following will suffice for the K+P side:

If there is only 1 winning move, make it

If advancing the pawn wins, advance it

Otherwise, select the king move that leaves the king furthest up the board. If that still leaves a choice, choose the move that leads to the least difference between king file and pawn file. If still a choice, choose the one that leaves the king nearest the edge of the board.

Similarly, reasonably sensible play for the lone king can be achieved by aiming to keep as close to the pawn as possible when faced with a choice.

These heuristics do not produce optimal play in the sense of always taking the fewest moves to win (or delaying the loss as long as possible), but they are intended to ensure a win is achieved whenever one is possible and sensible-looking play. I reserve the word 'correct' for such programs.

It seems computationally feasible to establish whether or not a given program for KPK is correct by systematically marking all positions that lie on winning sequences chosen by the algorithm in a manner analagous to the 'backing-up' method of Clarke (1975), which marked minimax values. This has not been done for the heuristics suggested here, though.

It should perhaps be mentioned that to achieve correct and good-looking play for KRK (Bramer 1975, Huberman 1968, Michie 1977, Zuidema 1974) appears to require more complex heuristics than for KPK. The difficulty in KPK resides mostly in deciding whether a win is possible, whereas in KRK almost all positions are wins and all the difficulty lies in choosing a move that wins rapidly.

ACKNOWLEDGEMENTS

I would like to thank Max Bramer for suggesting improvements to an earlier draft, and Danny Kopec for detecting misprints in the decision table.

REFERENCES

Bramer, M.A. (1975) *Representation of knowledge for chess endgames.* Report, Open University, Milton Keynes.

———(1977) *Representation of knowledge for chess endgames: Towards a a self-improving system.* PhD Thesis, Open University, Milton Keynes.

Clarke, M.R.B. (1977) A quantitative study of king and pawn against king, in *Advances in Computer Chess 1* (ed M.R.B.Clarke) pp.108-18. Edinburgh: University Press.

Harris, L.R. (1977) Listing of Algol program received privately.

Huberman, B.J. (1968) *A program to play chess endgames*. Technical report CS-106, Computer Science Department, Stanford University.

Michie, D. (1977) King and rook against king: historical background and a problem on the infinite board, in *Advances in Computer Chess 1* (ed M.R.B.Clarke) pp.30-58. Edinburgh: University Press.

Newborn, M. (1977) Peasant: An endgame program for kings and pawns, in *Chess Skill in Man and Machine* (ed P.W.Frey) chapter 6. Springer-Verlag.

Piasetski, L. (1977) *An evaluation function for simple king and pawn endings*. M.Sc Thesis, McGill University, Montreal.

Tan, S.T. (1972) *Representation of knowledge for very simple pawn endings in chess*. Report MIP-R-98, School of Artificial Intelligence, Edinburgh University.

——(1973) A knowledge-based program to play chess endgames, in *Proceedings of 'Chess playing by computer'*, Atlas Computer Laboratory, Chilton, Berkshire.

——(1974) *Kings, Pawn and Bishop*. Report MIP-R-108, Edinburgh University.

——(1977) Describing pawn structures, in *Advances in Computer Chess 1* (ed M.R.B.Clarke) pp.74-88. Edinburgh: University Press.

Zuidema, C. (1974) *Chess, how to program the exceptions?* Report IW 21/76, Mathematisch Centrum, Amsterdam.

A Representation for
Pattern-Knowledge in Chess Endgames

I.Bratko and D.Michie

ABSTRACT

A package known as AL1 (Advice Language 1) facilitates transfer of chess endgame knowledge to machine memory. Design is based on partitioning the problem-solving process into Advice (input: a board-state; output: an advice list) and Search (inputs: a board-state and an advice list; output: a forcing tree interpretable as a strategy for securing specified goals).

Assessment was made against test problems at two levels: (a) a problem which rates months of work to program by conventional methods, and (b) a problem which would otherwise seem too difficult to attempt at all. Results are reported with the elementary ending KRK, and with the more complex task of playing the ending KNKR. The behaviour in this problem domain of a strong tournament chess program was also investigated in order to compare both approaches to programming chess endgames: a lot of game-tree search plus general chess knowledge *versus* little game-tree search plus domain-specific knowledge.

Specifying knowledge using the AL1 language can be thought of as programming in a high-level assertional language. As this kind of programming is drastically different from programming in more usual languages it requires a special programming style. Experience with programming KRKN is discussed and a worked example presented which also shows a possibility of automatic generation of advice lists from sample games.

INTRODUCTION

The purely algorithmic concept of programming inherited from the era of small stores requires that a good program be short. The advent of large cheap immediate-access memories has directed attention to a different idea, namely that although programs can indeed be used as compact representations of bulky data-objects it is not necessarily true that the more compact the better. In order to reconstruct within acceptable running times the virtual data which they represent, they may have to spread themselves. For cases where purely algorithmic evaluation is too slow-running, by what principles can less compressed and more practical representations be found? Can we perhaps even retain purely algorithmic evaluation procedures and make additional material available to them in the form of 'advice', so that the procedures terminate in acceptable time?

The accumulation over centuries of books of 'advice' makes chess an illustrative case. Faultless machine play requires the evaluation of a function that has too bulky an extensional representation (more than 10^{45} megabytes) to make into a database and too long-running an intensional representation (about 10^{90} years on a micro-micro-second machine) for use in the form of a lookahead program. Yet the performance of chess-masters suggests that the computation may be a practical possibility. A master evaluates at a glance all but the 'interesting' positions, and these constitute a very small fraction of the total domain. With concentrated effort he can eventually evaluate most of this resistant fraction, leaving only a few 'hard' ones. Master play strives to create positions that are 'hard', at least for the opponent. But their prevalence in tournament records should not obscure their rarity in the total state-space nor the relative accuracy with which the master approximates the function in general.

Demonstrably, then, an evaluative device of impressive accuracy is constructible. Possibly even a completely accurate device could be built. Biological evolution has not done this. But why should it have? It has given the world many masterly flying creatures but has not achieved supersonic flight.

Table 1. Some information-processing parameters of the human brain. Estimation errors can be taken to be around 30 per cent.

1.	Rate of information transmission along any input or output channel	30 bits per second
2.	Maximum amount of information explicitly storable by the age of 50	10^{10} bits
3.	Number of mental discriminations per second during intellectual work	18
4.	Number of addresses which can be held in short-term memory	7
5.	Time to access an addressable 'chunk' in long-term memory	2 seconds
6.	Rate of transfer from long-term to short-term memory of successive elements of one 'chunk'	3 elements per second

Sources:
1. Miller (1956) summarises knowledge up to that date. Subsequent determinations are reviewed in any modern text in physiological psychology.

2. Calculated from 1 (see text)

3. Source cited by Funami and Halstead (1978)

4. 5 and 6. Sources cited by Chase and Simon (1973)

Table 1 gives approximate figures about the human brain as an information processer. Line 1 is valid within a factor of 2 for the range of sensorimotor tasks studied over the past few decades. Line 2 is derived from line 1, using generous assumptions concerning the fraction of information that is retained without loss and the amount of time per day that could be devoted to input of information about a given subject, such as chess. An objection to this method of derivation says that a man could *internally* generate and store more than the 10^{10} bits shown in the table by running the lookahead algorithm very fast in his head and storing the results, with or without conceptualisation into compressed form. But the third line of the table, which relates to the speed of mental operations, discourages this idea, as also do the remaining lines of the table.

So the brain of a chess-master, labouring under hardware limitations that are severe by present-day computing standards, evaluates to a respectable approximation a function that could not remotely be realised by pure algorithm alone nor by pure database alone on the fastest and largest imaginable computer. The brain of a trained spectroscopist performs a similarly 'impossible' feat when it evaluates the function that maps from mass spectra to molecular graphs. Here the attempt to mechanise using an advice-source to constrain an algorithmic procedure has scored successes. The only way to discover whether something of the kind is feasible for chess is to attempt it. Systematic exploration may require decades of work. We start with elementary endings such as those investigated by Huberman (1968: KRK, KBK, KBNK).

In addition to Huberman's, studies have been reported by Tan (1972: KPK; 1974: KBKP; 1977: pawns-only positions), Bramer (1975: KRK), Clarke (1977: KPK, KRK), Michie (1977: KRK on an infinite board), Harris (personal communication: KPK), Piasetsky (PhD thesis: KPK), Beal (personal communication: KPK), Bramer (1977: KPK), Perdue and Berliner (1977: KPK; KPPK; KPKP). Even these small domains conceal sufficient complexity to challenge existing methods for handling patterns and pattern-oriented strategies. This paper describes a computer language AL1 (Advice Language 1) designed to make these processes easier, with some results of its use.

ADVICE LANGUAGE: MOTIVATION AND STRUCTURE

AL1 (Michie 1976) was implemented in POP-2 on a DEC System 10 computer by members of the CS397.DM class at the University of Illinois during the Spring Semester of 1976. Authorship of the program modules described in this paper was as follows: *Table processing and editing*: Roger Haskin, Ian Stocks; *Search and move-generation*: Brian Foote, Jeff Gibbons, Paul Koning, Bill Lahti; *Chess description library*: Scott Preece, John Brockus, Bruce Copeland.

Four main themes motivate AL1:

1. Complex problems such as chess are not fully susceptible to uniform solution procedures. Such procedures have their place (resolution in theorem-proving, minimax search in games) but leave untouched the greater part of the problem, which concerns the representation of knowledge. This in turn presents a global and a local aspect. In chess the general-purpose 'evaluation function' embodies chess knowledge selected to be applicable and valid over the majority of cases. In the present work we emphasise the approach that decomposes each large complex problem into a mosaic of little problems, with each of which a separate package ('advice table') of specialised 'local' knowledge may be associated.

2. The mosaic representation subdivides the task of verifying the correctness of advice into checks between advice tables and checks within

tables, and decomposes the latter into cases. It also permits the combination of a number of advice tables into a single 'grand strategy' or 'policy' for a large problem, and permits advice to be modified and tables to be recombined.

3. Advice on how to tackle each 'little problem' takes the form not of sequences of actions but of lists of goals and move-constraints, from which strategies are separately generated by a domain-independent search program.

4. Programming as such is relegated to the bottom level of the design hierarchy and is confined to the implementation of predicates needed by the higher levels. Design of a policy proceeds 'top down' as shown in figure 1.

Figure 2 shows an appropriate stratification of the end-game KPKR (KPKR denotes the endgame in which 'our side' has the pawn; viewed from the opposite stand-point it would be written KRKP). Each arrow which denotes a nontrivial transition corresponds to one or more Advice Tables concerned with how the given transition can be forced. Some arrows expand into several precondition-postcondition pairs. Thus the three constituent phases of KQKR (following Fine 1964) might reasonably be handled by separate Tables:

1. Bring the kings together.
2. Force the enemy king to an edge of the board.
3. Face him with a choice between checkmate and separation of his king from his rook (followed by loss of the rook).

So far the ideas follow closely those of Huberman. Her concept of dividing progress into a succession of stages, each of which constitutes the goal of the preceding stage, can be compared with the successive levels of our advice lattice, except that we allow ourselves to jump levels. The essential feature of the 'stage' idea is that there is no slipping back to an earlier stage. Huberman introduced this one-way property at the level of detailed play of endings such as KRK. We retain it only at the level of global analysis for transitions between one Table and the next, as in the earlier cited sequence Phase 1 → Phase 2 → Phase 3 of KQKR. To effect this the analyst needs only to ensure that every postcondition logically excludes every higher-level precondition of the lattice. We do not apply the one-way principle when designing the fine structure of each individual Table. The principle is an analyst's tool; as a Table-writer's it is conducive to good style but is not mandatory.

The basic structure of the AL1 System is depicted in figure 3. The Problem solver (Search module) is concerned with the construction from an input position of a strategy in the form of a forcing tree. The Playing module implements the forcing-tree strategy in across-the-board play.

Knowledge contained in the Knowledge module is represented in the form of *Advice Tables*. The *Master Table* takes an input position through a list of preconditions and on finding a match routes it to the corresponding Advice Table. It thus functions as the Chairman of a 'committee of experts'. In our experiment the matching task was trivial. In a sophisticated case establishing a match (deciding which 'expert' should next be invoked) could be

defines a global policy as a lattice of
precondition-postcondition pairs.

constructs Advice Tables by inserting a
sequence of rules between the front and
back of each pair; each rule specifies
a condition pattern and advice-list;
when executed by AL1 it moves the state
of play nearer to the Table's post-
condition.

supplies truth-functional procedures
needed by the condition parts and the
advice parts of the rules.

Figure 1. Organisation of Advice-writing, using AL1. Preconditions and post-
conditions are defined only for 'Us-to-move' board-states.

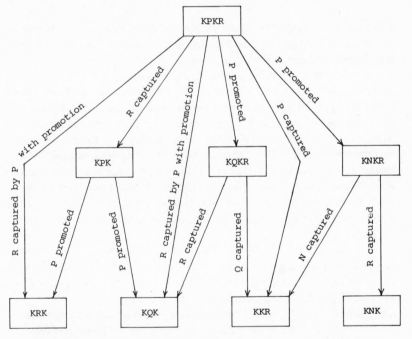

Figure 2. The player with king and pawn against king and rook may be able to
capture the rook or promote the queen, or he may be obliged to promote to
knight (giving check to buy time in order to avoid a skewer or a mate). Each
of these new situations brings desirable further situations into view. KPKR
and KQKR each presents a graded series of situations rating separate Advice
Tables, each situation being characterised by its own precondition and
postcondition.

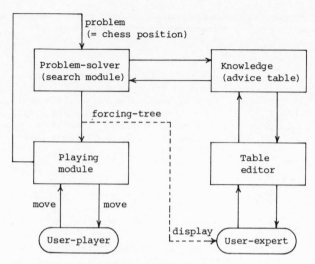

Figure 3. Basic structure of the AL1 System.
Knowledge and search are clearly separated.

elaborate: for example, evaluation of preconditions might require theorem-proving, as also might pattern-matching tasks encountered on occasion by the 'experts' (Advice Tables) themselves.

Transfer to a new Advice Table during play occurs when the old Advice Table's pre-condition ceases to hold, either because the Table's post-condition has been attained or because the opponent commits a blunder for which the advice-writer has not troubled to make specific allowance. In KQKR a particular Advice Table may, for example, be concerned with getting the enemy king to the edge of the board by employing forking threats against king and rook. If instead of yielding to *force-majeure* the opponent allows his rook to be taken, then exit from the Advice Table must occur, since 'overkill' has been achieved for which the Table made no prescription. Return to the Master Table will then re-route control to an Advice Table for KQK.

An Advice Table is a bundle of production rules for which the result of executing a rule is not an action, or anything explicitly to do with actions, but an 'advice list', each component of which indexes a 'piece of advice': *i.e.* a set of predicates expressing goals and constraints, together with a depth bound. It is left to the Search module, which knows nothing about chess but only about how to construct a forcing tree for stated goals and constraints, to work out a strategy for implementing the advice. Figure 4 reproduces an Advice Table for the KRK ending. The representation is so compact that, atypically, the Table consists of one rule only. Comparison may be made with figure 7, which shows an Advice Table for the KNKR game.

An advice list is a list of integers associated with an Advice Table rule. Each integer indexes a corresponding *piece of advice* in the repertoire.

A 'better' state is one which, if it is an 'Us-to-move' position, satisfies

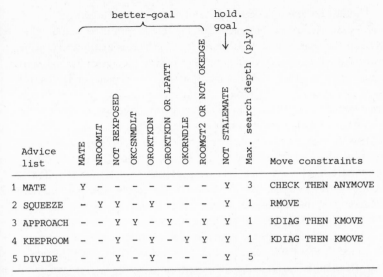

Advice list	better-goal MATE	NROOMLT	NOT REXPOSED	OKCSNMLT	OROKTKDN	OROKTKDN OR LPATT	OKORNDLE	ROOMGT2 OR NOT OKEDGE	hold. goal ↓ NOT STALEMATE	Max. search depth (ply)	Move constraints
1 MATE	Y	–	–	–	–	–	–	–	Y	3	CHECK THEN ANYMOVE
2 SQUEEZE	–	Y	Y	–	Y	–	–	–	Y	1	RMOVE
3 APPROACH	–	–	Y	Y	–	Y	–	Y	Y	1	KDIAG THEN KMOVE
4 KEEPROOM	–	–	Y	–	Y	–	Y	Y	Y	1	KDIAG THEN KMOVE
5 DIVIDE	–	–	Y	–	Y	–	–	–	Y	5	

Figure 4. The advice list for the KRK Advice Table. The goals are specified as a conjunction of indicated predicates listed along the top of the table. The Table plays for the stronger side, i.e. 'us against them'. All the goals are to be checked in them-to-move positions. Move constraints CHECK THEN ANY-MOVE mean: try first checking moves and then other moves.

the 'Us-to-move Better Goals' (UBG) of the given piece of advice and otherwise satisfies the 'Them-to-move Better Goals' (TBG).

The tree lookup conducted by the Playing module takes as input an Us-to-move board-state and a forcing tree. It finds the node on the tree with which this state matches and outputs the unique successor state (by definition a forcing tree does not branch on an Us-to-move node).

A forcing tree has the same sense as Huberman's use of the term. The tree is rooted in the input board-state which, in common with every other Us-to-move non-terminal node, has just one branch leading from it. In the present implementation each Them-to-move non-terminal node has as many branches leading from it as there are legal opponent's moves from the corresponding board-state. In addition:

1. Every Us-to-move terminal node satisfies the UBG, or in the case that no better-goal is specified, the node must be at the depth-bound in the tree.

2. Every Them-to-move terminal node satisfies the TBG, or in the case of no better-goal as above.

3. With the exception of the root-node every Us-to-move node (whether terminal or non-terminal) must satisfy the 'Us-to-move Holding Goal' (UHG).

4. Every Them-to-move node satisfies the 'Them-to-move Holding Goal' (THG).

5. The length of the longest branch does not exceed the depth-bound specified in the particular piece of advice which the forcing tree has been grown to satisfy.

This last feature is absent from the forcing tree of Huberman, who did not allow an attempt to construct a forcing tree to terminate with failure. In AL1, if the Search module saturates the depth-bound without yet having constructed a forcing tree, then control returns to the advice list and takes the next piece of advice from the list. A new search is then conducted using this. If the entire list is exhausted without the successful construction of a forcing tree, there has been a Table-writing error. Otherwise the first forcing tree to be successfully grown is taken as the strategy.

This strategy is then executed by the Playing module in across-the-board play up to a terminal node in the forcing tree, except for the cases that no better-goal is specified. In such a case there is no point in following the current strategy up to its end; instead, a new forcing tree is generated immediately on the next move. In this case the System is said to operate in the 'weak mode' as opposed to the 'strong mode'.

The following algorithm summarises the coordinate action of the Search module and the Playing module:

1. Read initial position P_0; set current position $P = P_0$; set MODE = *weak*
2. Set FT = empty tree.
3. Consult the Master Table and assign to variable T that Advice Table whose precondition is satisfied by P. If no precondition is satisfied then print 'No Table' and exit.
    4. If MODE = *weak* or there is no non-terminal node in FT equal to P then:
        4.1. If post-condition of T is satisfied in P then go to 2.
        4.2. Find in table T the first rule R from left to right such that P matches R. Assign to L the advice-list corresponding to R.
        4.3. Try in turn for pieces of advice A1, A2, . . . in L to generate a forcing tree satisfying the current piece of advice in position P until such a piece of advice Ai is found or the list L is exhausted. In the latter case output a message 'Table writing error' and exit.
        4.4. Set FT = forcing tree for advice Ai and position P. If Ai has no better-goal then set MODE = *weak* else MODE = *strong*.
5. Find in FT the node corresponding to the current position P. Output the move leading from that node in FT and update P by this move.
6. Read the opponent's move and update current position P by this move.
7. Go to 4.

The Search module proceeds depth-first at Us-to-move nodes and breadth-first at Them-to-move nodes. At the root node it only selects a branch if this is compatible with the move-constraints specified in the given piece of advice. At other nodes continuations are generated under the following conditions:

Case A: the node is an UTM node.

1. A legal continuation exists, and
2. the UHG is satisfied; otherwise the node is excluded from the set of candidates for incorporation into the final forcing tree, and

3. the UBG is not satisfied; otherwise the node is a candidate terminal node of the final forcing tree, and

4. the node's depth is less than the depth-bound specified in the given piece of advice.

Case B: the node is a TTM node.

Conditions 1-4 as above, substituting THG for UHG and TBG for UBG.

A Table editor allows the interactive user to add, delete and modify rules and to create new Tables.

RESULTS

For assessment of the package a *Type 1 problem* is one that ordinarily would take a great deal of time and effort to program. To pass this first test AL1 must make such problems appear easy. A *Type 2 problem* is one that would be intractable in terms of conventional programming.

Type 1 Problem: King and Rook *versus* King

Machine study of the KRK ending has a venerable history, recently reviewed by Michie (1977). Most pertinent is work by Coen Zuidema (1974), an International Chess Master and computer scientist. He does not state how many hours of work he put into programming KRK, but his Algol 60 program went through two versions of which the second amounted to nearly 400 lines of text. Moreover Zuidema complains of the difficulty and tediousness of the task, and especially of the work and augmentation of program text involved in introducing improvements. He comes, indeed, to a conclusion of sweeping pessimism in respect of chess programming generally:

'Our rook endgame has a start at two points.

1. The problem can be solved, it is evident that white wins, and it is anything but complicated.

2. A fairly good strategy is given. All the same, numerous small problems pop up. Improving the play entails a burden of program text.

So I have come to the conclusion that, given a reasonable strategy in a complicated game like chess, a continuous attempt to improve level of play will jam in proliferating details long before master level will have been reached.'

The Advice Table shown in figure 4 took a few days to write and check out. This Table was written with proof of correctness in mind and therefore the design principle was to keep its structure simple and suitable for proving it correct. Play is adequate but inelegant. Formal proof that it always mates from any KRK position within less than 40 moves has been obtained by Bratko (1978).

The Table atypically consists of one rule only, applicable to any KRK position. Associated with this rule is a list of five pieces of advice expressible as follows:

Provided always that stalemate is not created nor the rook left exposed,

1. MATE: look for a way to mate opponent's king in two moves;

2. SQUEEZE: if the above is not possible, then look for a way to further constrain the area on the chess-board to which the opponent's king is confined by our rook;

3. APPROACH: if the above is not possible, then look for a way to move our king closer to the opponent's king so as to help the rook in squeezing the opponent's king;

4. KEEPROOM: if none of the above pieces of advice 1, 2, 3 works, then look for a way of maintaining the present achievements in the sense of 2 and 3 (i.e. make a waiting move);

5. DIVIDE: if none of 1, 2, 3 or 4 is attainable then look for a way of obtaining a position in which our rook divides the two kings either vertically or horizontally.

An informal description of the predicates along the top of the Table in figure 4 is:

MATE: their king mated

NROOMLT: room to which their king is confined by our rook has decreased

REXPOSED: their king can attack our rook before our king can defend it

OKCSNMDLT: our king has approached to a critical square (in effect: to their king) so as to help the rook in squeezing

LPATT: the three pieces form an L-pattern: kings in opposition, and the rook next to our king and at the knight's jump distance to their king

OROKTKDN: rook divides the two kings

OKORNDLE: distance between our king and our rook has not increased

ROOMGT2: room to which their king is confined contains more than two squares

OKEDGE: our king on the edge

RMOVE: rook-move

KMOVE: king-move

KDIAG: diagonal king-move

Type 2 Problem: Defence of King and Knight *versus* King and Rook

Recent findings by Kopec and Niblett (1978) have greatly increased the estimated difficulty of the KNKR ending, which is usually thought to be a fairly straightforward draw. But the draw is not invariably agreed in tournament play and has on at least one recorded occasion slipped through a chess-master's fingers (Neumann — Steinitz, 1890, where Steinitz won due to opponent's error). Moreover treatments of this ending in the standard books have been shown by computational analysis to be inadequate and marred by errors. Kopec and Niblett's investigations, supported by experiments with human players, show that the KNKR problem, sometimes viewed as trivial, is so deep and complex that even masters must be said to have only a partial grasp.

The size of the space of legal positions, after drastic reduction by disregarding symmetric cases, is approximately three million. Another aspect of estimating the difficulty of the KNKR problem from a chess programmer's point of view is to consider the performance of a strong tournament program with KNKR. Experiments with a version of the world's leading tournament program, CHESS 4.5, described later in detail, showed that thanks to efficient search CHESS 4.5 was able to find a correct move in some difficult positions. But even in cases of relatively easy defence the lack of the specific pieces of knowledge 'Keep king and knight together!' and 'Preserve the centrality of the king!' could not be entirely compensated by the efficient and comparatively deep search to 7 or 8 ply.

Basic chess strategies applicable to the KNKR ending. The following is a shortened compilation from Fine (1964) and Keres (1974):

This ending is in general a draw. Database work (*see* Kopec and Niblett 1978; M. Gams, pers. comm.) shows that of the 1 347 906 legal rook's-side-to-move positions a slight majority, 696 414, are drawn. Of a similar number of knight's-side-to-move positions, approximately five-sixths are drawn. However, Black must stay in the centre of the board, because the won cases occur with the king in the corner.

What happens when the king gets to the corner is seen in figure 5.

Figure 5. 'Classical' example of a hard position for the weaker side in the KNKR ending.
White to play wins by 1 Kb6! Kb8 (or 1 ... Nc8+, 2 Kc7 Na7, 3 Rb8 mate), 2 Rb2!! Nc8+, 3 Kc6+ Ka8, 4 Kc7 and mate in at most two moves.
Black to play can draw by getting his knight out of the noose: 1 ... Nc8, 2 Rb3 (there is nothing better: on 2 Rb7 Nd6, 3 Rd7 Nc8, 4 Rd8 Kb8 White is nowhere.) Ne7!! (but not 2 ... Na7, 3 Kb6 as above, or 2 ... Nd6, 3 Kb6 and if 3 ... Kb8, 4 Kc6+) and if now 3 Kb6 Kb8, 4 Kc5+ Kc7 with a draw.

When the stronger side wins, one or more of the following strategies must be used:

1. Create mating threats.
2. Force the separation of king and knight.
3. Stalemate and capture the knight.

Figure 6 is a relatively easy example illustrating the combination of the above strategies. The most complicated variations occur where the knight is in the centre of the board, but can be stalemated because it is separated from its king. Mate threats are always involved in such cases. In general the play of winning positions is very difficult. By exhaustive enumeration Strohlein (1970) discovered examples in which the longest variations go to the depth of 27 moves until the knight gets finally captured.

Figure 6. An example illustrating the basic strategies for the stronger side. After 1 ... Nb7 (if 1 ... Nb3, 2 Rd1 and knight is stalemated and lost after next 3 Kb4), 2 Rd7 Kb8, 3 Kb6 Ka8, 4 Rh7! (better than 4 R   N ? stalemate), and now if 4 ... Nd8, 5 Rh8 and if 4 ... Nd6, 5 Rh8+ with mate in both cases.

The KNKR Advice Table. The task of the KNKR Advice Table (figure 7) is to cope with the threats illustrated in the previous section. Thus the basic long-term strategy is to prevent mating threats and to keep the king and knight together. Since mating threats occur only when the king is on an edge, the Table's aim is to preserve the degree of centrality of the king. If king and knight are already separated then the Table tries to bring them together. A short-term goal of the Table is of course to avoid the tactical pitfalls that would result in an immediate mate or loss of the knight.

The upper table of figure 7 is a KNKR Table constructed basically according to the above general design considerations. The only exception is that one of the positions belonging to the 'classical' example of a difficult defence with king in the corner (example of figure 5) is handled by a special rule, since in this case the only move that saves the game is in direct contradiction with heuristics that usually work (in the example of figure 5 this is move 2 . . . Ne7! of the second main variation).

The table specifies a classification of KNKR positions by means of rules in the feature space of POP2 predicates flanking the table:

OKEDGE: our king on an edge;

OKONSEP: our king and our knight separated (distance greater than 4 in king moves);

CORNCASE: corner case, positions that (possibly after some transformation, e.g. rotation) match the pattern of figure 8.

Pieces of advice indexed by the numbers in the advice lists are defined by the lower table of figure 7. The goals of separate pieces of advice are described by the use of the POP-2 predicates along the top of this lower table. These predicates, whose meaning is defined in detail in appendix 1, refer to the positions that occur in the analysis tree after possible continu-

ADVICE TABLE

Predicates	CR	R1	R2	ER
		Rules		
OKEDGE	–	N	Y	–
OKONSEP	–	N	N	–
CORNCASE	Y	–	–	–
	9	1	1	1
		2	5	10
		3	6	11
		4	7	12
		11	8	
			11	
			12	

Advice lists

ADVICE LIBRARY

Pieces of Advice	OKONNDLIT (u-t-m)	TRDEAD (t-t-m)	NOT MATE	NOT ONLOST	ONSAFE2P	TRDEAD OR CHECK	NOT ONOKATT	OKEDNDGE	OKCONDGE	OKCONDLE2	KINGSCLOSE	OKONDLE3	TKONDGT1	OKONDEQ3	Move constraints	Max. search-depth
	Better goals		us-to-move				them-to-move									
1. KILLROOK	–	Y	(Y)	Y	–	Y	–	–	–	–	–	–	–	–	CHECK THEN ANY	3
2. HOLD1	–	–	(Y)	Y	Y	–	Y	Y	Y	Y	Y	(Y)	Y	–	CHECK THEN ANY	4
3. HOLD2	–	–	(Y)	Y	Y	–	Y	Y	–	Y	Y	(Y)	–	–	CHECK THEN ANY	4
4. HOLD3	–	–	Y	Y	Y	–	Y	–	Y	Y	Y	(Y)	–	–	CHECK THEN ANY	4
5. HOLDEDG1	–	–	Y	Y	Y	–	Y	–	Y	Y	–	(Y)	Y	–	CHECK THEN ANY	4
6. HOLDEDG2	–	–	Y	Y	Y	–	–	–	–	Y	–	–	Y	Y	–	CHECK THEN ANY	4
7. HOLDEDG3	–	–	Y	Y	Y	–	–	–	–	–	Y	–	(Y)	–	–	CHECK THEN ANY	4
8. HOLDEDG4	–	–	Y	Y	Y	–	–	–	–	–	–	–	Y	–	–		4
9. CORNCASE	–	–	(Y)	(Y)	(Y)	–	–	–	–	–	–	–	–	Y	NMOVE	1
10. APPROKON	Y	–	Y	Y	Y	–	–	–	–	–	–	–	–	–	NMOVE OR ANY	4
11. SURVIVE1	–	–	Y	Y	Y	–	–	–	–	–	–	–	–	–		4
12. SURVIVE2	–	–	Y	–	–	–	–	–	–	–	–	–	–	–		2

Figure 7. The upper table is the KNKR Advice Table. The lower table shows 12 pieces of advice that are referred to by the Advice Table. Y's enclosed in brackets are logically implied by the other predicates selected in the same row. 'u-t-m' and 't-t-m' mean 'us-to-move' and 'them-to-move' respectively. By move constraints specification check moves are always considered first except for pieces 8-12. For precise definition of goal predicates see appendix 1.

ations. The goals of separate pieces of advice are defined as a conjunction of predicates marked 'Y' in a corresponding column.

In order to keep the playing time of the AL1 system for playing the KNKR ending within reasonable limits, the depth of search was limited to 4 ply, except for 1 ply for piece 9, 2 ply for piece 12 and 3 ply for piece 1. This limitation of search-depth proved to be very severe with respect to

Figure 8. The Corncase pattern. White rook is in one of the squares marked by R, Black to move. The only move that holds the position is Ne7!

discovering purely tactical traps. In order to maintain the shallow search and to rescue the program from suffering from tactical oversights, special heuristics were added for pattern-based handling of tactically undesirable situations. These heuristics, described by adding special pattern predicates to the holding-goals (ONSAFE2P, ONOKATT, KINGSCLOSE, TKONDGT1, see appendix 1), seem to compensate efficiently for a relatively shallow tree search in many cases. The example of figure 9 illustrates the pitfalls of shallow search and the subtlety of heuristics used to avoid them.

Other predicates test for the centrality of our king, the distance between our king and our knight, mate, and the presence of separate pieces on the board.

Except for the rule 'CR' that treats the 'corner case' by a more or less explicit hint for the correct move (advice CORNCASE), all other rules implement more general heuristics. They all try first to force a capture of the opponent's rook according to the piece of advice 1 (KILLROOK). Then, if this fails, if king and knight are not separated (rules R1 and R2), the table tries to hold as many desirable features of the position as possible by trying consecutive pieces of advice from the most ambitious to the least ambitious. If king and knight are separated (rule ER) then piece of advice 10 (APPROKON) calls for bringing them closer together. Finally, if all this fails, the least ambitious goals for bare survival (not worrying about the fate of the knight) come into operation.

Performance of the KNKR Advice Table. When testing the correctness of the Table, a variety of players, two of them of National Master strength (rated over 2300 on the international scale), engaged the system in play for a total elapsed time of more than 10 hours (about 150 moves on each side, starting from different positions). Three sequences of moves played by the Table (appendix 2) illustrate its typical behaviour under different circumstances:

1. The first sequence starts from a position with the weaker side's king in the centre of the board where the defence is comparatively easy. The Table is supposed not only to preserve a draw, but to preserve the degree of centrality of the king as well. The Table's king was pushed out

Figure 9. Rule R2 of KNKR Advice Table matches this position with the advice list 1, 5, 6, ... Since 1 (KILLROOK) fails, 5 (HOLDEDG1) is tried. Features NOT ONOKATT (not our knight our king attacks) and TKONDGT1 (distance between their king and our knight is greater than 1) are specified conjunctively with other features forming holding-goal in them-to-move positions. This piece of advice succeeds in producing the correct move Nc8. Before predicates NOT ONOKATT and TKONDGT1 were added to this holding-goal the advice table played Nc6? not observing within the 4-ply search that after 1 Nc6? Kd6, 2 Ne7 Rh8+ White gets mated on the next move.

of the strict centre, but the Table succeeded in keeping its king within the 16 central squares. It seems that it is theoretically not possible to keep the king in the KNKR ending within the 4 central squares, but 16 squares provide enough manoeuvring space to resist a further pressure toward an edge of the board.

2. The second experiment starts from a position with the king next to the edge. In this situation it is harder to avoid the king being pushed right to the edge since there is less safe space for the knight to manoeuvre, but the Table still succeeded in holding the next-to-edge position.

3. The third trial started from a position with the king on the edge, given by Keres (1974) as an example of difficult defence (figure 11). In this game the Table was walking on the edge of a precipice, safely passing many critical positions, among them being the 'classical' variation of figure 5, and the critical position from the tournament game Neumann — Steinitz where the player with the knight went wrong.

These results gave a strong indication that the Table was correct. But later a class of special positions (Kopec, pers. comm.) was discovered, in which the only correct continuation worsens the separation of king and knight while an immediate try to bring them closer fails because of tactical reasons. An example is shown in figure 10. As the design of the Table was based on the assumption that a separation of king and knight like Nc3 in figure 10 leads necessarily to loss, the Table tries in such positions to recover the separation by any means, which fails. No position has been found where the Table plays inadequately if the distance between king and knight is less than 3. In addition, empirical testing supports the conclusion that the Table preserves the draw indefinitely, provided that play *starts* from a theoretically drawn position with the king-knight distance less than 3, even

Figure 10. Black to move. Nf6+ would immediately bring K and N closer together, but Nc3+ is the only drawing move.

though the separation may on occasion be allowed temporarily to increase.

When playing the KNKR ending on the PDP-10 computer the present implementation of AL1 spends on average about one minute of computer time per move, mostly due to the comparative inefficiency of the forcing-tree generation routine. The program examines about 10 nodes in the game-tree per second. When run on comparable machines, other chess-playing programs, e.g. CHESS 4.5 (Slate and Atkin 1977) or MASTER (Birmingham and Kent 1977) examine at least a few hundred positions per second. A new version, AL2, will achieve increased run-time efficiency, among other improvements. But considering AL1's efficiency from the point of view of programmer productivity, these experiments give evidence of great savings. Table-writing and check-out for KNKR occupied one of us (I.B.) for less than six weeks. We doubt whether play of a similar standard, especially if 'centrality preservation' is to be included, could be programmed using standard methods in less than a substantial multiple of this figure other than by promoting large proliferations of forward search. As an annotation on this last remark, we present results, kindly supplied by D. Slate, of having the leading U.S. tournament program CHESS 4.5 play the KNKR game against an expert opponent from selected starting positions. These results illustrate the behaviour of 'general' chess programs (general in the sense of playing all phases of chess game), embodying general chess principles, or heuristics, hopefully applicable to a large majority of chess positions, rather than position-type specific knowledge.

Performance of CHESS 4.5 Tournament Program with KNKR
CHESS 4.5 was required to defend the weaker side of KNKR against a human opponent rated just over 2000 on the U.S. Chess Federation scale, i.e. an 'expert'. The program ran on a CDC 6400 machine, on which it was able to win the 1976 ACM Computer Chess Championship (more recently it won the 1977 World Computer Chess Championship on the much faster Cyber 176). CHESS 4.5's general evaluation function was used without allowing any adjustment or special 'tuning' to the KNKR problem. Search depth was set to 7 ply. Since forced variations are searched beyond this

pre-set horizon, moves 8 ply deep were occasionally searched in the present case. Under these conditions, CHESS 4.5 typically looked at a few tens of thousands of nodes per move and spent up to 120 seconds per move, typically between 30 and 60 seconds.

In the three trials described below, play started from the positions used in the experimental validation of the KNKR Table.

Figure 11. White to move

1. A 'classical' difficult defence (Fine 1964; Keres 1974) with the weaker side's king in the corner. CHESS 4.5 found correctly the move considered most difficult in the books, but then stumbled on the fourth move of the main 'book' variation, obtaining a lost position. Starting from the position of figure 11 (Keres 1974) with CHESS 4.5 as Black the play went:

1	Rb2+	Ka1	
2	Rb8	Ne2!	(the move considered to be most difficult)
3	Kb3	Kb1	
4	Re8	Nd4+?	(Keres gives 4 ... Nc1+)
5	Kc3	Nb5+	(if 5 ... Nf3, 6 Re3 separating K and N definitely)

Play actually stopped here, but Black is lost as the further analysis shows: 6 Kb4 Nd4, 7 Re4 Nc2+, 8 Kc3 Na3 (if 8 ... Kc1, 9 Re2 wins), 9 Re1+ Ka2, 10 Re2+ Kb1, 11 Kb3, and White wins.

2. Figure 12 shows another difficult position, with the weaker side's king on the edge (Keres 1974). CHESS 4.5 playing Black found the only correct defence against the main line given by Keres (exclamation marks by Keres):

1	Rb7	Nh6
2	Rh7	Ng8!

In a game Steinitz — Neumann (1890, with colours reversed), Black wrongly continued 2 ... Ng4 and lost after 3 Rh4 Ne3, 4 Re4 Nd1, 5 Rf4+ Kg7, 6 Rf3 Kg6, 7 Ke5 Kg5, 8 Kd4 Kg4, 9 Rf1 Nb2, 10 Rb1 Na4, 11 Rb4 winning the knight.

3	Rf7+	Ke8
4	Rg7	Kf8!
5	Rh7	Ke8

| 6 | Rf7 | Nh6 |
| 7 | Rf1 | Ng8 |

This preserved a draw. Or, as also tried, instead of 7 Rf1:

| 7 | Rg7 | Kf8 |

Figure 12. White to move   *Figure* 13. Black to move

3. A further position (figure 13) taken from our own tests, with the weaker side's king in the centre (easiest defence). CHESS 4.5 playing Black allowed its king to be driven to the edge resulting in a harder defence. This enabled the opponent to create mating threats, and after additional weaker moves by the program the king and knight got separated, leading to a lost position. The game went:

1	...	Kf5	
2	Kc4	Nh4	
3	Kd4	Kf4	
4	Rf2+	Nf3+	
5	Kd3	Kg3	
6	Ke3	Ne5	
7	Rf8	Kg4	
8	Ke4	Nc4?	(after this Black is already lost; better is 8 ... Ng6)
9	Rg8+ (10)	Kh5	(now king and knight are separated. Number 10 in brackets following Rg8+ means that after this move White can mate or win the knight in 10 moves, as checked by the exhaustive database for the KRKN ending.
10	Kd4?		(10 Rd8! wins)
		Nd6	(position is drawn)
11	Ke5	Nc4+?	(does not care about joining king and knight. Nf7 draws)
12	Kf4 (10)	Nb2 (9)	
13	Rg5+ (8)	Kh6 (7)	
14	Kf5 (11)		(Rb5! wins easily)
		Nc4 (11)	

15	Kf6 (?) (22)	Ne3 (22)	
16	Ra5?	Ng4+	(drawn)
17	Kf7	Nf2	
18	Ra1	Ng4	

Position is drawn again and play was terminated. Although starting from an easy drawn position, the program, lacking fundamental knowledge about the KNKR ending, was wandering from one lost position to another which its human opponent failed to exploit. This last example shows that starting from any KNKR position a sneaky player can probably always induce the program to disjoin king and knight and get into a lost position. The program's global evaluation function sees no reason why king and knight should not be separated!

It is interesting to observe that the program's opponent, although an expert, after achieving theoretically won positions never grasped the opportunity actually to defeat the program. This has a bearing on the level of difficulty of this sub-domain.

DISCUSSION

Formulating Strategies in Advice Language 1

Advice Language, via its mechanisms of better-goals, holding-goals, and move constraints, provides various ways of guiding the search when generating a detailed strategy, i.e. a forcing-tree. In this section we outline some basic approaches to exploiting the potentialities of these instruments.

By specifying rule patterns one can classify the domain handled by a table into classes of positions, or stages of play, to which the same overall ideas are applicable. Also, exceptions or special cases can be handled in a natural way by specifying appropriate rules.

A very powerful tool from the table writer's point of view is the mechanism of the advice list that works as: Try to force the achievement of goals specified by the first piece of advice in the advice list; if this is not achievable (no corresponding forcing-tree exists) then try the next piece in the list, etc. Thus the table writer need not bother too much with a precise definition of types of positions in which something is achievable or not. What is important is to order pieces of advice in a list so that the most ambitious goals come first. This guarantees the play toward the most desirable goal out of the achievable ones.

Move constraints are supposed to be used basically in order to improve the *efficiency* of forcing-tree generation. But, as ordering of candidate moves can be achieved via move constraints, this instrument can be used also for achieving *correct* play.

Since the forcing-tree generation module examines the 'us-moves' in a depth-first manner the resulting forcing-tree is not always optimal with respect to achieving a goal in the smallest number of moves. If optimal play in this sense is required, the table writer himself can achieve this by controlling the order of search in a somewhat artificial way and at the expense of the computational efficiency of the system. Namely: the piece of advice in question can be multiplied in such a way that subsequent copies have greater maximum search-depths.

Two examples taken from the KNKR table will illustrate the utilisation of goals in describing search heuristics. The first of them will reveal how search efficiency can be improved by goal specification. The second example presents a model of the table-design process using knowledge contained in chess books. That example also shows the possibility of automatic creation of advice tables from sample games.

Consider the piece of advice KILLROOK of the table in figure 7. The main objective of this advice is to force the capture of opponent's rook in the KNKR ending, if possible. Therefore the better-goal in them-to-move positions is TRDEAD (their rook dead). The depth of search is limited to 4 ply (effectively 3 ply because them-to-move positions occur only at odd levels), since if this goal cannot be forced within 3 ply it cannot be forced at all. This specification is sufficient to produce correct play, but the following addition increases the search efficiency of this piece of advice by a typical factor of more than 10. The capture of their rook can be forced only by immediate captures or by forking their king and rook with our knight, i.e. checking their king. Also, the better-goal cannot be achieved if our knight is lost without compensation. Therefore we drastically constrain the search by specifying:

> us-to-move holding-goal: NOT ONLOST
> them-to-move holding-goal: TRDEAD OR CHECK

In the next example consider the design of the advice list for the rule R2 (OKEDGE AND NOT OKONSEP). Assume that the predicates for specifying goals are already known (predicates in the top of the lower table of figure 7), e.g. from the previous design of rule R1, as was the case in the actual design of our KNKR table. Now the question is to specify an appropriate advice list to guarantee correct play while never searching deeper than 4 ply. For this purpose we can use chess-book examples of correct defence. In our example we follow a variation given by Keres (1974) starting from the position of figure 12. Assuming a 4 ply deep search we try to find, for each correct move a simplest and weakest goal specification that still produces that move.

> 1   Rb7   Nh6

All other moves lead to immediate mate or the loss of the knight; therefore for this move suffices the following specification of holding-goal in us-to-move positions (UHG for short):

> UHG: NOT MATE AND NOT ONLOST
> 2   Rh7   Ng8

Specification

> UHG: NOT MATE AND NOT ONLOST

is sufficient to suppress all faulty second Black moves (Ke8, Nf7, Nf5, Kg8) except for 2 ... Ng4 which after 3 Rh4 leads to the subsequent loss of the knight. To suppress Ng4 we can specify a them-to-move holding-goal (THG):

> THG: OKONDLE3
> 3   Rf7+   Ke8

The only move.

    4   Rg7   Kf8!

A 4 ply search with

    UHG: NOT MATE AND NOT ONLOST

produces the correct move 4 ... Kf8 as the analysis shows the refutation of
4 ... Nh6 with respect to UHG within 4 ply: 1 ply: Nh6, 2 ply: Rg6, 3 ply:
K anywhere, 4 ply: R captures N (ONLOST), *or* 3 ply: N anywhere, 4 ply:
Rg8 MATE.

    5   Rh7   Ke8

    UHG: NOT ONLOST

    6   Rf7   Nh6

    UHG: NOT ONLOST

    7   Rg7   Kf8

    UHG: NOT ONLOST; THG: OKONDLE3

(to suppress 7 ... Kd8 and 7 ... Ng4)

    8   Kf6   Ng8+

Here UGH: NOT ONLOST and THG: OKONDLE3 suppress all incorrect
moves but 8 ... Nf5. After 1 ply: Nf5, 2 ply: Ra7, 3 ply: Nd6, 4 ply: Ra8+
White is winning while the above UHG and THG are not violated. To
remedy this we can, using another already existing predicate, modify THG
into:

    THG: OKONDLE3 AND TKONDGT1

    This last modification of THG does not affect previous moves; thus a
sufficient advice to handle the above variation from Keres (1974) is one
with no better goals and

    UHG: NOT MATE AND NOT ONLOST

    THG: OKONDLE3 AND TKONDGT1

    The above process can be viewed as a process of pattern-specification
using the goals device, such that the resulting pattern-description econ-
omically extracts correct forcing-trees from game-trees to the prescribed
depth. In this way the above example also shows the possibility of mechan-
ising the table-writing task, provided that basic predicates are known in
advance. However, the task of efficient automatic formation of predicates
(related to 'concept formation') seems much harder. The work of Negri
(1977) and Michalski and Negri (1977) shows some promise in this last
respect.

    Additional treatment, similar to the above, of another (even shorter)
book variation proved that sometimes it is crucial to hold OKONDLE2
(instead of OKONDLE3) and OKCONDGE (the distance between our king
and the nearest corner must not decrease). This led to the splitting of the
piece of advice to handle rule R2 into a list of pieces of advice of decreasing
preference resulting in the one of figure 7. The book examples used in the
construction of this advice list proved to be highly relevant since during
experimental testing only one position was misplayed by this advice list.
This was very easily fixed by adding to THG another already existing desirable pattern: NOT ONOKATT.

    It is important to note that the holding-goals of the KNKR table *do
not* yet characterise the class of drawn positions as one might understand.

When no better-goals are specified (which is our case), the AL1 system plays in the so-called 'weak mode' which means that after each move the advice table is consulted again and a new forcing-tree generated. Therefore a better understanding of the way holding-goals function is: the feasibility of holding these goals for the next 4 ply guarantees that the position after the *first* ply is still drawn.

Some Defects of AL1

Besides other smaller defects of AL1, the next version, AL2, must remove the following major ones:

(1) Forcing-tree generation must be fast. Besides more efficient coding, a stronger ordering of candidate moves would be extremely helpful:

    (a) ordering according to move constraints where preference is explicitly stated in the advice;

    (b) according to general common-sense heuristics try first capturing moves, checking moves, 'killer' moves according to the 'killer heuristic' (see Birmingham and Kent, 1977), attacking moves.

(2) In the specification of goal predicates a special facility for consulting the Advice Table (recursive re-entering of the Advice Table) and generating a forcing-subtree should be available.

(3) Playing in the 'strong mode', where the strategy contained in the forcing-tree is executed up to the actual achievement of the better-goal, can lead to serious oversights after a bad opponent's move creates unexpected opportunities. Therefore the current better-goal should be rechecked before 'blindly' following the existing forcing tree: it should be checked if a stronger better-goal can be achieved after the opponent's reply. This calls for a (possibly partial) ordering of the set of better-goals contained in the table.

(4) Application of a list of similar pieces of advice with goals of decreasing ambition is performed independently piece by piece, which can cause a repeated search through the same parts of the game-tree. Instead, it should be possible to define such a series of pieces of advice in a more compact way by specifying a single goal in the form:

⟨ P1 *then* P2 *then* P3 *then* .... ⟩

Application of such a piece of advice should result in producing a forcing-tree for 'the best achievable' of P1, P2, P3, ...

(5) Move constraints that can at present be specified only for the top level of the game-tree should be available at other levels too, optionally different at separate levels.

(6) In order to improve the conciseness of Advice Tables, holding-goals global to the table should be introduced, to be interpreted in conjunction with particular holding-goals.

(7) The depth of a node in the search-tree should be explicitly available to the table-writer since it is often reasonable to think about goals that vary by the node level.

CONCLUDING REMARKS

Whether or not encouragement for chess programming more generally can be drawn from just one Type 1 and one Type 2 result depends on what relation holds between the factor of labour-saving conferred by AL1 and the complexity of the domain. If this factor increases as complexity increases, then the signals are set fair. The question can only be answered by experiment. A positive conclusion would be an immediate stimulus (a) to seek order-of-magnitude speed-ups by machine-coding critical procedure-bodies, by introducing pruning constraints at Them-to-move nodes of the search, and by using special hardware to exploit the parallelism inherent in many of the constituent processes; (b) to attempt a domain complex enough to demand the construction of a complete multi-level policy as an integrated hierarchy of several Advice Tables; (c) to give attention to methods of proving correctness of such policies based on piecemeal proofs of their constituent Tables.

ACKNOWLEDGMENTS

Part of this work was done while one of us (D.M.) was on leave of absence from the University of Edinburgh. Thanks are due to Professor Jim Snyder, Chairman of the Department of Computer Science in the University of Illinois at Urbana, for the hospitality of his Department and for provision of computing and other facilities. Hard and gifted work was done by the students named in the text, who also contributed design innovations. Special acknowledgment is due to another member of the class, R. Roloff, who introduced the advice list, in place of a single piece of advice, as the output of an Advice Table rule. We thank D.Slate of Northwestern University who ran the tests using CHESS 4.5, and D. Kopec for playing against the KNKR Advice Table during many test runs.

Acknowledgment is made to the Research Community of Slovenia for enabling the two authors to come together in Edinburgh for a six-month collaboration, and to the British Council for their good offices in making machine time available on the Science Research Council's Interactive Computing Facility. We also thank the University of Dundee for computing time and facilities.

REFERENCES

Birmingham, J.A & P. Kent (1977) Tree searching and tree pruning techniques, in *Advances in Computer Chess 1* (ed. M.R.B.Clarke) Edinburgh: University Press.

Bramer, M.A. (1975) Representation of knowledge for chess endgames. Technical Report. The Open University: Faculty of Mathematics (Milton Keynes, UK).

Bramer, M.A. (1977) Representation of knowledge for chess endgames: toward a self improving system. Ph.D. Thesis, Open University, Milton Keynes, UK.

Bratko, I. (1978) Proving correctness of strategies in the AL1 assertional language. *Information Processing Letters 5*, 223-30.

Chase, W.G. & H.A. Simon (1973) Perception in Chess. *Cognitive Psychology 4*, 55-81.

Clarke, M.R.B. (1977) A quantitative study of King and Pawn against King, in *Advances in Computer Chess 1* (ed. M.R.B.Clarke). Edinburgh:University Press.

Fine, R. (1964) Basic Chess Endings. New York: McKay (1st edition 1942).

Huberman, B.J. (1968) A program to play chess end games. Technical report no. CS 106. Stanford University: Computer Science Department.

Keres, P. (1974) Practical Chess Endings. London: Batsford Ltd.

Kopec, D. & T. Niblett (1980) How hard is the play of the KNKR ending? This volume.

Michalski, R.S. & P.G. Negri (1977) An experiment on inductive learning in chess end games, in *Machine Intelligence 8* (eds. E.W.Elcock & D.Michie). Ellis Horwood-Wiley.

Michie, D. (1976) An advice-taking system for computer chess. *Computer Bulletin*, ser. 2, *10*, 12-14.

Michie, D. (1977) King and Rook against King: historical background and a problem on the infinite board, in *Advances in Computer Chess 1* (ed. M.R.B.Clarke). Edinburgh: University Press.

Miller, G.A. (1956) The magical number seven, plus or minus two: some limits on our capacity for processing information. *Psychol. Rev. 63*, 81-97.

Negri, P.G. (1977) Inductive learning in a hierarchical model for representing knowledge in chess end games, in *Machine Intelligence 8* (eds. E.W.Elcock & D.Michie). Ellis Horwood-Wiley.

Perdue, C. & H.J. Berliner (1977) EG — a case study in problem solving with king and pawn endings. *Proceedings of the 5th Int. Joint Conf. on Artificial Intelligence*, 421-7. Cambridge, Massachussetts.

Slate, D.J. & L.R.Atkin (1977) CHESS 4.5: The Northwestern University chess program, in *Chess Skill in Man and Machine* (ed. P.Frey). New York: Springer Verlag.

Strohlein, T. (1970) Untersuchungen über Kombinatorische Spiele. Dissertation for Dr. Rev. nat. Munich: Technische Hochscule.

Stroud, J.M. (1966) The fine structure of psychological time. *Ann. N.Y. Acad. Sci.* pp. 623-31, cited by M.H. Halstead (1978) in Elements of Software Science, Elsevier.

Tan, S.T. (1972) Representation of knowledge for very simple pawn endings in chess. Research Memo MIP-R-98, Department of Machine Intelligence, University of Edinburgh.

Tan, S.T. (1974) Kings, pawn and bishop. Research Memo MIP-R-108, Department of Machine Intelligence, University of Edinburgh.

Tan, S.T. (1977) Describing pawn structures, in *Advances in Computer Chess 1* (ed. M.R.B.Clarke) pp.74-88. Edinburgh: University Press.

Zuidema C. (1974) Chess, how to program the exceptions? *Afdeling informatica* IW 21/74. Amsterdam: Mathematisch Centrum.

Appendix 1. Goal-Predicates used in the KNKR Table

In the definitions of goal-predicates we use the following abbreviations:

OK	our king (= king of the weaker side)
ON	our knight
TK	their king
TR	their rook
CURPOS	current board position to which advice is applied (to become the root of the forcing-tree)
NEWPOS	any position contained in the forcing-tree except for CURPOS

Function $dist(p1, p2, pos)$ gives the distance in king moves between pieces $p1$ and $p2$ in position pos.

The predicates used in the KNKR table:

MATE	the side to move is mated
CHECK	the side to move is in check
TRDEAD	their rook is dead
ONLOST	our knight lost without compensation, i.e. possibility of capturing their rook or of stalemate
ONSAFE2P	our knight safe 2 ply: checks for some very obvious patterns (pinning, forking) in which the weaker side is to move and cannot avoid the loss of the knight within 2 ply
ONOKATT	our knight attacks our king: an undesirable pattern because the mobility of our knight is limited by its own king
OKEDNDGE	$dist(OK,$ nearest edge, NEWPOS$) \geqslant dist(OK,$ nearest edge, CURPOS$)$
OKCONDGE	$dist(OK,$ nearest corner, NEWPOS$) \geqslant dist(OK,$ nearest corner, CURPOS$)$
OKONNDLT	$dist(OK, ON, NEWPOS) < dist(OK, ON, CURPOS)$
OKONDLE2	$dist(OK, ON, NEWPOS) \leqslant 2$ or $manhdist(OK, ON, NEWPOS) \leqslant 3$ where $manhdist$ is distance in king moves if king is only moved in 'rook directions'
OKONDLE3	$dist(OK, ON, NEWPOS) \leqslant 3$
OKONDEQ4	$dist(OK, ON, NEWPOS) = 4$
TKONDGT1	$dist(TK, ON, NEWPOS) > 1$
KINGSCLOSE	$dist(OK, TK, NEWPOS) \leqslant dist(OK, ON, NEWPOS)$

In special cases where ON is dead or TR is dead the pattern-predicates return the favourable value since the loss of material is treated explicitly by predicates TRDED and ONLOST.

Appendix 2. Sample Games Played by the KNKR Table

The following three games were played, among others, by the KNKR Advice Table of figure 7 as White against American Master Danny Kopec rated over 2350.

Game 1. Initial position of figure 13 with colours reversed, king within 16 central squares. 1 Kd5 Rf2, 2 Ke4 Rg2, 3 Kd5 Rg4, 4 Ne5 Rf4, 5 Nc6 Kd3, 6 Ne5 Ke3, 7 Nc4+ Kd3, 8 Nd6 Rh4, 9 Ke5 Ra4, 10 Ke6 Ra5, 11 Ne8 Kd4, 12 Nf6 Rg5, 13 Kd6 Re5, 14 Nd7 Ra5, 15 Ke6 Rg5, 16 Nf6 Rg1, 17 Kf5 Rf1+, 18 Ke6 Rf4, 19 Nd7 Re4+, 20 Kf5 Re1, 21 Nf6 Re5+, 22 Kf4 Rb5, 23 Ng4 Rb4, 24 Kf5 Rb1, 25 Ke6, play interrupted since Black was making no further progress.

Figure 14. White to move

Game 2. Initial position of figure 14, king next to the edge.
1 Nh6 Rf8, 2 Kg6 Ke5, 3 Kg5 Rf1, 4 Ng4+ Ke6, 5 Nh6 Rf6, 6 Ng4 Rf5+, 7 Kg6 Rb5, 8 Nh6, play interrupted, Black was not able to drive white king to the edge.

Game 3. Initial position of figure 12 with colours reversed, king on the edge. 1 Nh6 Rh7, 2 Ng8 Rh1, 3 Kg7 Rg1+, 4 Kh7 Kf7, 5 Nh6+ Kf8, 6 Nf5 Rg5, 7 Nh6 Rg7+, 8 Kh8 Ra7, 9 Ng4 Kf7, 10 Kh7 Ra4, 11 Nh6+ Kf6, 12 Ng8+ Kg5, 13 Kg7 Ra7+, 14 Kf8 Kf5, 15 Ke8 Rg7, 16 Kf8 Ra7, 17 Ke8 Ke6, 18 Kf8, play interrupted, position is a draw.

How Hard is the Play of
the King-Rook-King-Knight Ending?

D. Kopec and T. Niblett

ABSTRACT

An exhaustive database of the KRKN ending revealed inadequacies in the published analyses. It was also used (see appendix 3) to demonstrate that the domain can be mastered by an endgame expert after special study. Experiments with Class 'A' players showed that the defence of the draw for the knight's side is in general easier than demonstration of the win for the rook's side, but that a special class of positions exist for which the correct defence runs counter to most players' intuition. The nature of these positions is examined, and modifications are proposed to existing KRKN theory.

INTRODUCTION

The subject of the first part of our paper is a database for the KRKN endgame. The second part reports experiments with human players in the same endgame. The third discusses the main concepts for the domain.

USE OF A DATABASE TO INVESTIGATE THE KRKN DOMAIN

By 'database' we mean a complete computer-stored look-up table for optimal play. Such a database has already proven invaluable for the study of KPK (Clarke 1977). With its help Bramer (1977) has proved the optimality of a program to play this endgame. Using a database for KRK, Clarke (1977) has shown that White can force a win from any position in 16 moves or less — instead of 17 as was previously thought (Fine 1941). These endings however are ones for which Chess Masters have no difficulty in finding correct, if not optimal moves. We think this is due to the small number of 'patterns' needed to assess any position statically, despite the longest win being 19 moves for KPK, 16 for KRK. Very little lookahead seems to be needed for these endings.

KRKN is different: here we enter a domain that can be challenging even for a master. This is a subgame of chess which is possible to compute fully by machine (a database), but very hard for the unaided person to play correctly. The ending KQKR illustrated a similar case recently when two International Masters repeatedly failed to find a winning line in play against a data base for this ending. We have had similar results with KRKN against master-strength players.

Other databases already constructed are those for KRPKR and KQPKQ (Arlazarov and Futer 1979), the latter being notoriously difficult even for leading Grandmasters. Last year Grandmaster Bronstein, once challenger for the world championship, had a position with KQPKQ at adjournment and used the database to find a win he himself could not. Although KRKN is simpler than this, one of our later examples shows the breakdown of 'pattern matching' even for a Grandmaster. The major difference then between this endgame and KPK is the need for very much more tree-search, or lookahead by humans.

KRKN databases have a fairly long history. The first of which we are aware was completed in 1970 by Thomas Strohlein (1970) as part of a Ph.D. Dissertation on Graph Theory and Combinatorics. Recently Ken Thompson of Bell Labs computed databases for all the interesting four-piece endings including KRKN, and Gams (1978) has computed specifically the KRKN case and has partially validated Thompson's work. Finally at the M.I.R.U. we have independently constructed one. With this we can check one database against another to ensure correctness. This is a major problem with databases: because of their size only machine checking is possible and even this is daunting. In the case of Grandmaster Bronstein's consultation of the KQPKQ database, the actual line he was given would have resulted in a draw due to a database error at the very end!

Algorithm for Database Construction

Michael Clarke (1977) has already described a procedure for KPK. However, KRKN differs slightly, for breadth-first backing up is used. The procedure can be conveniently divided into three parts (see figure 1).

All positions for White where he can mate immediately or win the black knight in one move are defined as won at depth 1. The first step is to find all these without loss of the rook or stalemate. For each legal BTM position a counter is set for the number of illegal successors. This completes the initialisation.

Backing up from WTM positions won at depth N is done by finding all legal predecessors of the position. Since there are $8 + 8 = 16$ potential moves in all, the counter will show the value 15 at the moment that the set of legal moves is exhausted. If any hasn't previously been marked as won, then if the counter has value 15, that position is marked lost depth $N + 1$; otherwise the counter is incremented by 1.

Backing up from BTM positions is simpler. Again all legal predecessors are found. Any not previously marked as won are marked as won depth N.

Results

The procedure described above was executed as a program on the DEC System-10 computer. The resulting database was used to partially check the correctness and completeness of Thompson's KRKN database. The latter was the one actually used for most of the results now to be reported.

It is difficult to estimate the exact number of legal positions. Due to symmetry it is much less than 64^4. Thompson (private communication) estimates 741 000 drawn positions and 651 000 positions won for White in the canonical state space.

Note that the backing-up method described entails that only won

A *White-to-move (WTM) position* is won depth = 1 if White can
mate or win the knight without stalemate or loss of the rook

Backing up from BTM positions

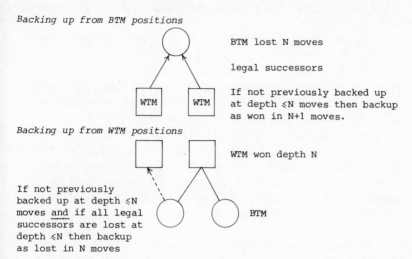

BTM lost N moves

legal successors

If not previously backed up
at depth ≤N moves then backup
as won in N+1 moves.

Backing up from WTM positions

WTM won depth N

If not previously
backed up at depth ≤N
moves <u>and</u> if all legal
successors are lost at
depth ≤N then backup
as lost in N moves

BTM

Figure 1

Depth of loss (moves)	No. of positions
1	378,518
2	95,450
3	46,269
4	30,729
5	20,055
6	15,071
7	11,740
8	9,495
9	8,562
10	7,415
11	6,308
12	5,356
13	4,133
14	3,356
15	2,290
16	1,621
17	1,333
18	1,046
19	727
20	556
21	458
22	373
23	302
24	178
25	111
26	18
27	2

Figure 2. The distribution of losses with depth

positions are assigned a depth in the database. Draws are recognised by lack of this marker. There is, incidentally, one position lost for White! There are therefore roughly 1 400 000 legal positions with White to move. This is about 15 times larger than KPK. The distribution of losses with depth, WTM, is shown in figure 2.

The two extreme positions lost in 27 moves with optimal play are:

WK:d1   WR:h1   WK:c1   WR:f8
                and
BK:b1   BN:g4   BK:a3   BN:e2

(For optimal winning sequence see appendix 1.) It is important to realise that these winning lines are far longer than needed for any position given in the literature. The deepest win we have been able to find as a published position is 16 moves with optimal play. The database can be used to generate (a) optimal play for White from any won starting position, (b) optimal play for Black from any lost starting position, (c) correct play for Black from any drawn position. Safe knight-capture is counted as 'win' without considering play of the residual KRK game. This section concludes with a discussion of KRKN as it is represented in the literature.

Analysis of Previously Published Treatments of KRKN

The history of KRKN is peculiarly long, peculiar in that the king, rook and knight move in the same way as in the ancient game of Chaturanga, which is otherwise very different from Chess. Several theoretical positions can be dated to the ninth century AD. In English the two most comprehensive treatments of the endgame are in Fine (1941) and Averbakh (1978). Fine's analysis is based on that of Berger whereas Averbakh relies on many more sources. Fine however gives a more detailed analysis for each position.

Figure 3. Black to move

To show the difficulty of the ending and its 'opacity' even in the face of extensive analysis we discuss the position shown in figure 3. This position is a variant of that given for Chaturanga by al-Adli in the ninth century. It was rediscovered in 1859 and (incorrectly) analysed in 'The Chess-Players Chronicle'. Berger subjected the position to detailed analysis, and this was used by Fine in 'Basic Chess Endings' and continued by several analysts. The database shows that it can be won in 14 moves.

To show the difficulty of analysis we give Fine's main line (his punctuation) for the first few moves, comparing his move with that of the KRKN database:

1	. . .	Na5+	forced
2	Kb5	Nb7	all optimal
3	Rf8!	. . .	Rh5 is best, one move shorter.

Here Fine's notes say 'Not ... Rh7, because of ... Kb8, Kb6 drawn'. However Kc6 wins, and more quickly than Fine's main line. This is one of two cases where Fine gives the wrong game-theoretic value for a position.

3	. . .	Nd6+	forced
4	Kc6	Nc4	
5	Rd8!	. . .	In spite of Fine's exclamation mark, this move changes the depth of win from 11 to 17 moves in this position.

This demonstrates a typical phenomenon. The human master finds a plan which preserves the game-theoretic value of the position, but which is inefficient in the minimax sense.

We have analysed all the main lines given in Fine, and figure 4 illustrates the results. It is superficially surprising that there are so few non-optimal moves at large depths and so many at relatively shallow depths. However, if the win is very deep there is usually only one good winning move. At depths of 7-10 moves the master doesn't try in his tree searching to find optimal moves, just good ones. At lower depth still he can see through to the end.

Using the database we have seen that optimal play is very hard to find, even for the analyst. There is a small subset of the position space, the longer wins (17 to 27 moves deep), which has never been explored. Masters have great difficulty in winning these positions. In our small-scale trials of human play against Thompson's database (not with full tournament time allowance) we never saw it done. Subsequently, however, similar but more systematic tests were convincingly passed by A.J. Roycroft, not a Master but a specialist in the chess endgame study. His own account is reproduced as appendix 3.

EXPERIMENTS WITH CLASS 'A' PLAYERS

Further information about the nature of the difficulties was obtained from experiments with Class 'A' players described below, in which the database did not figure.

Experiment I : Weak Class 'A' Players
Objectives. This experiment was to discover:
(a)   How hard is it for an 'A' player to win a won position?
(b)   How hard is it for an 'A' player to draw a drawn position?
Usually when humans are asked about this ending they will say either that they know nothing about it, or that it is drawn by keeping the king and knight close together and avoiding the edge of the board where mating threats can occur. Since Class 'A' players are better than average tournament

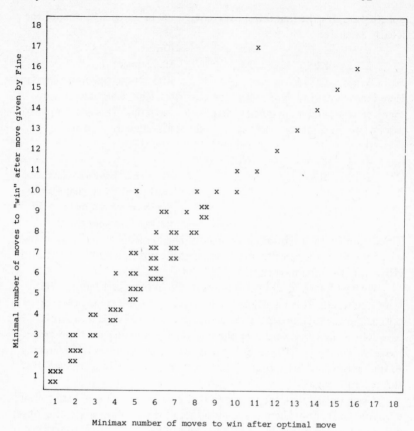

Figure 4a. All positions White to move

players, and are likely to know just the two above concepts, their performance on both the stronger and weaker side, under tournament-like conditions, was thought worth investigating.

Experimental Design. Three subjects, all university students averaging
1882 in ELO rating, were each assigned two positions, one drawn, which
they were to defend with the knight's side, and the other won which they
were to win for the rook's side. Drawn positions included starting positions
from which testing was done on Ivan Bratko's Advice Table (see Bratko
and Michie, this volume). All these positions have in common the mutual
proximity of the defending K and N. However in 'Corncase', (see figure 5),
after 1 Rb2+ Ka1, 2 Rb8, we reach the only position which Bratko had to
program as a special case, since only 2 ... Ne2, separating K and N as much
as possible in the position, draws.

Won positions were selected as the longest (not necessarily main-line)
variations given in Fine's *Basic Chess Endings*, reportedly requiring 24, 17
and 15 moves to win (see figure 5, T4, T5, T6). Later checking of these
positions with the Thompson database revealed that they actually require
14, 9 and 11 moves to win, with optimal play for both sides. Subjects were

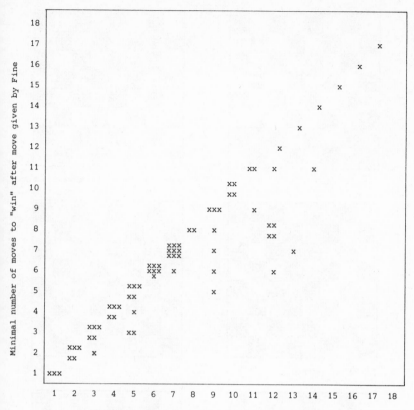

Figure 4b. All positions Black to move

assigned positions based on a predetermined rank-ordering of their difficulty. Proficiency was demonstrated by holding the game-theoretical value over 30 moves of play in one hour against a U.S. Master opponent (D.K.). Otherwise resignation, imminent checkmate, or a loss of material were the termination conditions.

Results and Conclusions. These Class 'A' human subjects had no difficulty defending typical drawn KNKR positions except for 'Corncase', where the subject later testified that he had played the correct 'separating' move without knowing why the other moves lost. The experimental design and results are summarized by figure 6. On the stronger side subjects failed in two of three cases to win. The one subject who did win, did so in 11 moves, 6 less than in the variation given by Fine, but Fine gives 17 moves for T5, i.e. 6 more than 11! A later check against the Thompson database showed that optimal play requires 9 moves (see appendix 2).

The database also showed that the experimenter's knight's-side defence in the experiment was suboptimal in the minimax sense.

Immediately following the experiment, a complete analysis was done to discover all game-theoretic value-changing moves (i.e. 'mistakes'). Since

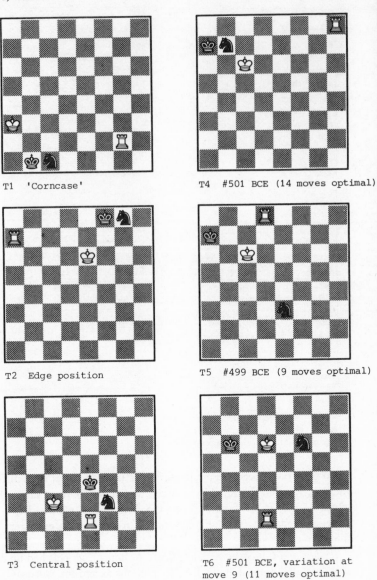

T1 'Corncase'

T4 #501 BCE (14 moves optimal)

T2 Edge position

T5 #499 BCE (9 moves optimal)

T3 Central position

T6 #501 BCE, variation at move 9 (11 moves optimal)

Figure 5. The positions for Experiment I. T1, T2, T3 are drawn positions and T4, T5, T6 are won positions. (BCE stands for *Basic Chess Endings* by R.Fine.)

subjects held the draw in all three cases, it was only a question of whether the human opponent had failed to exploit some error which they had made, but no errors were found. When subjects failed to win won positions, their errors occurred quite early in the sequences. The retrospective analysis of the continuation from position T6 proved to be most interesting. After: 1 Rb2+ Ka5 2 Kc6? (2 Re2 was correct) Ne4, is this position a draw or a win for White?

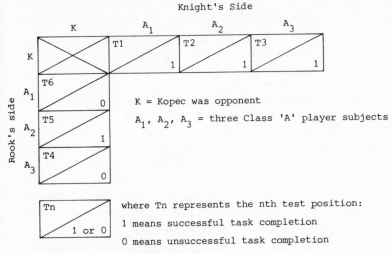

Knight's Side

K = Kopec was opponent

A_1, A_2, A_3 = three Class 'A' player subjects

where Tn represents the nth test position:

1 means successful task completion

0 means unsuccessful task completion

Figure 6. Design and results of Experiment I

Figure 7. Continuation from T6 of Experiment I with subject P.Edwards.
Is this position a draw or a win for White?

At first 1 Rb3! was tried, when not 1 ... Ka4?, 2 Rd3! and Black is
lost, but 1 ... Nd2, 2 Rd3 Nb1! etc. when the position is clearly drawn.
Then 1 Kd5 was tried with some very surprising variations to follow, but
we will let readers study the position longer before giving the variations
which provide the answer. This retrospective analysis led to the discovery
of three positions where counter-intuitive 'separating' moves were required
to draw and the Bratko Advice Table erred. The failure of the Table for
these positions was not really surprising, for it had been designed for
positions where the BK and BN were relatively close together (i.e. < 3 king
moves apart) with the belief that all positions where K and N are further
separated are either lost or, if not, K and N must approach each other
immediately. This is the view which had been presented in all the basic
chess literature for this ending. Positions where K and N are reasonably
separated were considered lost. Only recently, thanks to Mr A.J.Roycroft,
have we learned of a Czech paper by Mandler (1970), which indicates that
work has been done on this aspect. These positions, which at the time were

believed to be new to the theory of this ending, led to an entire benchmark of 16 positions where K and N are separated. Some of these positions will be discussed in the last part of this paper, but now we will discuss their importance in Experiment II.

Experiment II: strong Class 'A' players

Objectives. Subjects' performance in the defence of KNKR in Experiment I pointed to the conclusion that it was not a difficult task for Class 'A' players. However the retrospective analysis brought new interest to the problems of correct play in drawn positions with the domain much richer than previously thought. Experiment II was seen as necessary to find out just how hard is the defence of KNKR when the domain is enriched with these 'new' positions, or more specifically: How well will strong Class 'A' human players defend KNKR positions where counter-intuitive 'separating moves' are required as well as other concepts?

Experimental Design. The 16 positions generated by the retrospective analysis of Experiment I and tests on the Bratko Table included 13 positions which the table did not handle correctly. For Experiment II nine of the hardest KNKR positions were selected, with highest ranking in difficulty going to positions where counter-intuitive 'separating' moves were required. Further ranking was based on the number and complexity of concepts considered necessary for correct play. Three Class 'A' players, with ratings of 1950, 1975 and 1915 were each allotted three positions in such a way as to approximately even out the mean ranking of difficulty and to include for each subject a reasonable diversity of concepts necessary for correct play (figure 9). The nine positions used are given in figure 8. Viewing them from left to right, top to bottom, we go from the position highest ranked in difficulty (D3) to the lowest ranked (D15). Note that D3, D2, and 'Corncase' all require counter-intuitive 'separating' moves, and thus are highest ranked. Since D3 includes D2 as a subset of correct play from it, but first requires a 'natural' knight move, it is higher ranked than D2. The method by which these nine positions were ranked is given in figure 9. Of these nine positions the Bratko Advice Table had failed to play the correct move in seven of them, handling 'Corncase' and D15 correctly.

Subjects and experimenter (D.K.) were allowed 40 minutes in which subjects were to play 20 moves which held the draw. The time had been slightly curtailed compared with Experiment I since once subjects succeeded in playing the first few moves correctly the task became easy and rather pointless. According to their post-mortem testimonies, two of the three subjects in this experiment knew that they should keep K and N together.

Results and Conclusions. As shown in figure 10, subjects failed in 6 of 9 trials. Failure in 4 of the 5 positions highest ranked in difficulty indicates that our *a priori* notion of what comprises a difficult KNKR position for the human was probably correct. However subjects played the first unforced move correctly in 5 of the 9 positions. In addition, we note that despite subjects' correct handling of 'Corncase' in both Experiment I and

Figure 8. The nine positions used for experiment II, with D3 ranked hardest, going left to right, top to bottom to D15 ranked lowest. (Black to play in each except 'Corncase'.)

Experiment II, it is apparent from post-experimental questioning that subjects did not do the necessary calculation to see why the 'separating' move, 2 ... Ne2 was the only move which did not lose.

This experiment substantiated our notion that at least expert and perhaps master strength human play may be required for the correct defence of KNKR. We have also gained insight into specific concepts which may be necessary for correct play in positions where defending K and N are separated.

Positions were allotted to subjects in such a way as approximately to even out the mean ranking of difficulty, and at the same time to include for each subject a reasonable scatter. Symbols such as OKON, ONLOST2P, etc., are explained in the glossary below:

APPROKON: 'approach our king our knight'. *Piece of advice* needed to guide our knight or our king in separated positions

Position name	Rank	Concepts involved	Subject treatments	Average rank
D3	1	APPROKON ? *		
D2	2	? *	A$_1$:D3,D6,D10	4.67
Corncase	3	OKONDE4 (special case)		
D4	3	APPROKON COMMON GROUND		
D10	5	ONLOST2P OKONNDLE	A$_2$:D2,D13,D15	5.33
D13	6	OKTRATT ONLOST2P		
D9	7	APPROKON ONTRNDLE †		
D6	8	OKTRATT	A$_3$:D4,Corncase,D9	4.33
D15	8	OKTRATT		

* These are positions which require "separating" moves whose underlying concepts we have been unable to specify.

† Note that during Experiment II it was discovered that if White plays Kc4 after 1 ... Nc6+ the addition of OKONNDLE would be necessary.

Figure 9. Ranking of positions for Experiment II (average rank 4.77)

ELO RATING

D3	0	D6	0	D10	0	A1	1950
X							

D2	0	D13	1	D15	1	A2	1975
X							

D4	0	CORN-CASE	1	D9	0	A3	1915
X				X			

Di = a drawn benchmark position

1 = task successfully completed

0 = task unsuccessfully completed (subject lost or resigned)

X = first unforced move was a losing one

Figure 10. Design and results of Experiment II.
Kopec was experimenter in each case.

OKONDE4: 'our king our knight distance equals 4'

Common Ground: Potential meeting squares for K and N in separated positions.

ONLOST2P: 'our knight lost 2 ply'. Predicate which detects nearly all losses of our knight in two ply. Applied as 'Not ONLOST2P'.

OKONNDLE: 'our king our knight new distance less than or equal to'. Means that we are happy to maintain or decrease the distance (in king moves) between our king and our knight, but not increase it

ONTRNDLE: 'our knight their rook new distance less than or equal to'. Intended to prevent our knight from approaching their rook in separated positions

OKTRATT: 'attack their rook two ply'. Predicate for positions where our king threatens to capture their rook thereby allowing common ground or some other concept to be attained

CONCEPTS INVOLVED IN
A BENCHMARK OF 20 DRAWN POSITIONS
Counter-Intuitive 'Separation' and Common Ground

In this section we discuss some of the positions used in Experiment I and Experiment II, as well as a few others.

On the basis of the insight gained we augmented the set of 16 positions mentioned earlier with a further four with the aim of establishing a benchmark of 20 positions. These should specifically test all the features of difficulty of which we were aware. Returning to figure 7 from the experimental run with subject P.Edwards, after 1 Kd5 we reach the position labelled D2 (see figure 8). To answer our earlier question, 'What is the value of the position in figure 7?' we now need a 12-ply search, i.e. 1 ... Nc3+, 2 Kc4 Ne4, 3 Re2 Nd6+ (any other N move gets the knight stranded as well), 4 Kc5 Nb7+, 5 Kc6 Nd8+ (if 5 ... Ka6, 6 Ra2+ Na5+, 7 Kc5 and wins), 6 Kc7 Nf7, and now the knight is clearly stranded. Instead, in position D2 the only drawing move is 1 ... Nf6!! We shall give Black's responses to all of White's possible K moves from figure 11, in counter-clockwise order: if (a) 2 Ke6 Ne4 (b) 2 Kd6 Ne4+ (c) 2 Kc6 Ne4 returning to figure 7 (d) 2 Kc5 Nd7+ or Ne4+ (e) 2 Kc4 Nd7 (f) 2 Kd4 Nd7 (g) 2 Ke5 Nd7+. Returning to D2 (figure 8), after 1 ... Nc3+?, 2 Kc4 Ne4, if White plays 3 Kd4? instead of 3 Re2, we have D3 (figure 8), when only 3 ... Nd6 draws. Then if 4 Kc5 Ne4+, 5 Kd5, we return to D2, and so D3 is a superset of D2, whereby first the 'natural' Nd6+ is required, and later the 'counter-intuitive' Nf6+!! (D2). Considering D2, after 1 ... Nc3+?, 2 Kc4 Ne4, we try 3 Rb5+? Ka6, 4 Rd5 reaching D4. Normally White's last few moves comprise part of a winning technique which entails: (1) separate BK and BN, (2) drive N further away, (3) trap N and win it. However in D4, Black has the drawing move Kb7 threatening Nf6 ... Ne8, ... Nc7 or ... Nf6, ... Kc7, and Nd7. (Other threats are ... Kc6 or ... Kc7 and ... Nd6, or Nf6 and Nd7 to follow.) White's inability to prevent all these 'paths' by which BK and BN threaten to meet, ensures that Black can draw. We have labelled these meeting squares 'Common Ground'. Figure 12 depicts this concept for D4

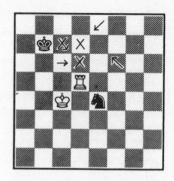

Figure 11. Position arising from D2 after 1 ... Nf6+!! This is the first case from our experimental work where a counter-intuitive 'separating' is required.

Figure 12. Position after 1 ... Kb7 from D4. Squares which are 'Common Ground' or potential meeting squares for BK and BN are marked with an X. Paths to these squares are marked with arrows also indicating approximate direction to target square(s).

after 1 ... Kb7, 'paths' denoted by '↑' and the Common Ground denoted by 'X'. Another heuristic indicating the move ... Kb7 is 'If K and N are 3 or more K moves apart, don't move your K onto a file or rank where N can move'. Otherwise that N move can be met by a R move forking K and N.

If in D4 Black tries 1 ... Kb6?, then 2 Rd4! wins, i.e. 2 ... Nc5 and 2 ... Nf6 both lose to 3 Rd6+ and after 2 ... Ng5, 3 Rg4 Nf7, 4 Rg6+ Ka5, 5 Kd5 Nd8, 6 Rg8 Nb7, 7 Kc6 and wins.

In 'Corncase', the refutation to Black's other N moves after 1 Rb2+ Ka1, 2 Rb7 deserves more attention than the continuation after the correct move 2 ... Ne2. This might go: 2 ... Na2, 3 Kb3 Kb1 (if 3 ... Nc1+, 4 Kc2 wins), 4 Rb8!!.

In post-mortem discussion those two subjects who played the correct 2 ... Ne2 did not mention the passing move 4 Rb8 as the refutation of Na2. The idea of a 'passing' move is the only way White can win in the position. Then on 4 ... Nc1+, Kc3+ with 6 Kc2 to follow, wins. 2 ... Nd3, 3 Kb3 and then if 3 ... Nc5+, 3 ... Nb2, or 3 ... Nc1+, 4 Kc2 wins quickly.

'Guided Knight Tours'

Next we shall consider D9 and D10 (figure 8). In D10 Na4 and Ne4 are the candidate moves. Na4 is closer to the BK than Ne4 but on the edge, while the latter move is more centralized. In fact after 1 ... Na4, 2 Kb4 forces 2 ... Nb6 since Nc3 loses to 3 Rg2+ (ONLOST2P), and then Black's N is stranded with further separation from the BK to follow. Correct is 1 ... Ne4 when White can make no progress, though Black must still play very carefully, i.e. if 2 Kd3 Nc5+, 3 Kc4 repeats the position; or if 2 Kd4 Nd2 (not Nc3? Rg2+, etc.) 3 Rg2 Kc1 and we have the typical 'edge draw'. In D9 the candidate moves are obviously Nf5+ and Nc6+. Both moves bring the N a distance of five king moves from the BK; however Nf5 offers no further path back to the BK. After 1 Nf5+, 2 Ke5 Ne7, 3 Rh6 the N is stranded and soon will be lost. Even after the correct move, 1 ... Nc6+, 2 Kc4, the BN still needs careful guidance − is 2 ... Na5+ or Ne5+ correct? This decision and the one on Black's first move can be guided by the important underlying heuristic 'When N and K are separated, don't move the N towards both the opposing K and R unless it is the only way back to your K'. Thus here the correct move is 2 ... Na5+ and after 3 Kb4 Nc6+ it is clear Black cannot be forced to further separate K and N. If 2 ... Ne5+?, 3 Kd5 Nd7, 4 Rh6 and again the N is stranded.

OKTRATT for Common Ground

The last group of positions from Experiment II to be discussed is D13, D6 and D15 (figure 8). These all share the idea of OKTRATT (our king their rook attacks) in order to allow 'Common Ground' to be achieved.

In D13 there are two drawing moves. 1 ... Kc7 and 1 ... Nd2. 1 ... Kc7 is clearer joining K and N next move. If 1 ... Nd2 then 2 Rb8+ Kc6! draws.

Similarly, in D6 1 ... Kc8 allows 'Common Ground' to be achieved via either ... Nf6 or ... Nd6. This is the only move since 1 ... Nf6? is met by Rd6 forcing further separation. In D15 Black's 'normal' move, 1 ... Ng3 is thwarted by 2 Re3 when 2 ... Nf5 is impossible due to the fork, 3 Re5+ and thus the knight is quickly lost. In order to avoid the fork and still allow a path for 'Common Ground' via 2 ... Ng3 or 2 ... Ne3, depending on how White plays, the 'separation' move 1 ... Ke6 draws. The more obscure 1 ... Nh2 also draws because White cannot cut off both the paths ... Nf3 and ... Ng4 to follow.

D8 (figure 13) was contrived to show that the distance between K and N is not as important as the availability of paths between them, especially for the N. Both the moves ... Nb5 and ... Nc6 bring the BN closer to the BK, though at the same time closer to the WR and WK. Yet these are the only moves to consider, for a K move would be too slow in joining BK and BN, i.e. 1 ... Ke2, 2 Kc4! Nc6, 3 Re8+ and the N is soon trapped. Comparing 1 ... Nc6 and 1 ... Nb5, we see that the former is more centralized, offering two clear paths through the centre (... Ne5 and Nd4) back to the BK. White cannot prevent both these 'threats' and thus Black draws easily with 1 ... Nc6. On the other hand, 1 ... Nb5 only offers ... Nd4+ as a direct path back to the BK, with ... Nd6 as an indirect route. The natural move, 2 Rd8, cuts off these two possibilities (see figure 13, D8.2). Yet ... Nc7 draws! After 1 ... Nb5? from D8 it was later found that 2 Kc4! Nd6+, 3 Kd3 wins. From D8.2 White is threatening Rd7 and then Kb4 winning the N. Black's only way out of this is to play ... Nc7 immediately, before the N gets 'fenced in'. The N wanders, persistently evading the R. If the WK tries to participate, the BK comes to the rescue of the N just in time, or the N escapes back to the BK. From D8.2 if we continue 1 ... Nc7, 2 Rd6 Kf2, 3 Rf6+! Kg3 (the only move − if 3 ... Ke3, 4 Kc4 and 5 Rc6 wins quickly) 4 Kc4, then the position D18 is reached. Here only 1 ... Kh4 draws. The explanation for why 1 ... Kg4 loses can be given as an extension of the heuristic given for D4, 'If K and N are separated by a distance of 3

D8 BK and KN are quite separated, but 1 ... Nc6 draws easily

D8.2 White threatens Rd7 and Kb4 winning the N. The 'unusual' 1 ... Nc7! draws

D18 Another possible successor of D8. Only the surprising 1 ... Kh4 draws

Figure 13. Some other positions from our benchmark. D8.2 and D18 are successors of D8.

or more K moves, don't move your K onto a file or rank which the N may need to occupy in two moves', i.e. 1 ... Kg4?, 2 Rc6 Ne8, 3 Re6 Ng7 (3 ... Nc7, 4 Re7 wins the N soon), 4 Rg6+ and wins.

CONCLUSIONS
How hard is the KRKN ending?

1. The use of an exhaustive database has shown that published treatments of KRKN are marred by serious inaccuracy and incompleteness. Hence the domain cannot be described as easy, even for the chess analyst.

2. The attacking side's task in won positions is too hard for successful play to be reliably demonstrated by Masters against optimal defence. But a celebrated endgame study specialist was able to do this after intensive preparation on a benchmark of six 24-movers, only three of which had been made available to him for prior study (see appendix 3).

3. Play of the defence of king and knight against king and rook in drawn positions is easier than play of the attacking side in won positions. But even the defence proved to be too hard for strong Class 'A' players to conduct reliably.

4. Most of the difficulty of the defender's task is concentrated in a relatively small class of positions which demand counter-intuitive moves separating king and knight.

5. The key concept of separation between king and knight should not be measured geometrically as has been customary. A revised definition should be based on multiplicity as well as length of available paths between the two pieces.

6. The KRKN ending is a great deal harder than has been assumed, and its complete codification has eluded chess theorists. Improvement of existing theory is here put forward. This was substantially aided by availability of the KRKN database.

ACKNOWLEDGEMENT
This work was done by the authors as graduate students in the Machine Intelligence Research Unit at Edinburgh University under the

supervision of Professor Donald Michie, whose substantial assistance in the preparation of this paper is hereby acknowledged. One of us (T.N.) also acknowledges financial support from a Science Research Council studentship.

Dr Raymond Carhart gave valuable programming advice during the construction of the database.

REFERENCES

Arlazarov, V.L. & A.V. Futer (1979) Computer analysis of a Rook endgame, in *Machine Intelligence 9* (eds. J.E.Hayes, L.I.Mikulich & D.Michie). Chichester: Ellis Horwood, and New York: John Wiley.

Averbakh, Y. (1978) *Rook against Minor Piece Endings*. Batsford.

Bramer, M.A. (1977) Representation of Knowledge for Chess Endgames: towards a Self-Improving System. *Ph.D. Thesis*. Milton Keynes: Open University. See also this volume.

Clarke, M.R.B. (1977) A quantitative study of king and pawn against king, in *Advances in Computer Chess 1* (ed M.R.B.Clarke) pp.108-18. Edinburgh: University Press.

Fine, R. (1941) *Basic Chess Endings*. New York: David McKay Company.

Gams, M. (1978) Constructing complete game strategies. *Undergraduate thesis*. Ljubljana: University of Ljubluana Faculty of Electrical Engineering (in Slovenian).

Mandler, A. (1970) *Studie. II.Svazek*. Prague: Edice Sachoveho Klubu Ustredniho Domu Armady.

Strohlein, T. (1970) Untersuchungen über Kombinatorische Spielen. *Ph.D. Thesis*. Munich: Technische Hochscule München.

**Appendix 1. Optimal Move Sequences
for the Two Longest Wins**

Position: WK:d1, WR:h1, BK:b1, BN:g4

1	Rh4	Ne5	2	Re4	Nf7	3	Rb4+Ka2
4	Kc2	Ka3	5	Kc3	Nd6	6	Rb6 Ne4+
7	Kd3	Nf2	8	Kc4	Nd1	9	Rb3+Ka4
10	Rf3	Nb2+	11	Kc3	Ka3	12	Rg3 Na4+
13	Kc4	Ka2	14	Kb4	Nb2	15	Rg4 Nd3+
16	Kc3	Nc5	17	Rc4	Ne6	18	Ra4+Kb1
19	Ra5	Ng7	20	Re5	Ka2	21	Kd4 Kb3
22	Kd5	Kc3	23	Kc6	Kd4	24	Kd6 Kd3
25	Ke7	Kd4	26	Rg5	etc.		

Position: WK:c1, WR:f8, BK:a3, BN:e2

1	Kd2	Nd4	2	Kc3	Nb5+	3	Kc4 Nd6
4	Kc5	Nb7	5	Kb6	Nd6	6	Rf4 Kb3
7	Kc5	Nb7+	8	Kc6	Nd8+	9	Kb5 Ne6
10	Rf3+	Kc2	11	Kc4	Kd2	12	Rf5 Kc2
13	Rf2+	Kd1	14	Kd3+Nc5+		15	Kd4 Nb3+
16	Kc3	Ke1	17	Rb2	Nc5	18	Kd4 Ne6
19	Ke3	Kf1	20	Rb6	Nc7	21	Ke4 Kf2
22	Ke5	Ke3	23	Rb7	Na6	24	Kd6 Kd4
25	Rb6	Ne5	26	Rb4	etc.		

Many positions, for either side, have more than one optimal continuation. The above two lines should therefore be regarded as specimen paths excerpted arbitrarily from two optimal-strategy trees.

Appendix 2

When given the position WK:c6, WR:d8, BK:a7, BN:e3(#499, BCE)
(see figure 5, T5) for the stronger side in Experiment I, the subject, Pat
Coleman (1965 rating), improved on the variation given by Fine by 6 moves.
What follows is the experimental record:

W: P.Coleman B: D.Kopec	Minimax-Optimal Value (Moves)	Optimal move(s) and their minimax-optimal path-lengths
1. Rd4 (13)*	9	
1. ... Nf5	6	Kb8(9)
2. Ra4+ (15)	6	
2. ... Kb8	5	
3. Re4	5	
3. ... Ka7	3	Ng3(5)
4. Kd5	8	Kc7(3)
4. ... Kb6	8	Nb3, Kb7, Kb6
5. Ke6 (21)	7	
5. ... Ng3	7	
6. Re1	6	
6. ... Kc5	5	Kc7, Kc6(6)
7. Ke5 (22)	4	
7. ... Kc4	4	
8. Kf4	3	
8. ... Nh5+	3	
9. Kg5	2	
9. ... Ng3	2	
10. Kg4 (25)	and captures N	

* Figures in brackets after White's moves in this column are the total time
from the allotted hour, consumed by subject.

Appendix 3

The following notes are contributed by A.J. Roycroft, author of *Test-tube Chess* and editor of EG, the international endgame study magazine.

The task was simply this. I was presented with three positions known to be won for the side with the rook in a battle against a lone knight, and I was to win them. The diagrams R1, R2 and R3 show the positions, and this is how the play went from each.

R1			R2			R3		
1.	Rb3	Ka5	1.	Ke5	Na4	1.	Ke7	Kg7
2.	Kc7	Nf2	2.	Rh7+	Ke8	2.	Ra3	Kg6
3.	Kc6	Na4	3.	Kd6	Nb6	3.	Ke6	Nc2
4.	Rf3	Nd1	4.	Rh8+	Kf7	4.	Rg3+	Kh5
5.	Kc5	Nb2	5.	Rh4	Nc8+	5.	Kf5	Kh4
6.	Rh3	Nd1	6.	Kd7	Nb6+	6.	Rc3	Ne1
7.	Kc4	Nb2+	7.	Kc6	Nc8	7.	Kf4	Ng2+
8.	Kc3	Ka3	8.	Rh7+	Kf6	8.	Kf3	Kh3
9.	Rg3	Na4+	9.	Rh6+	Kg7	9.	Ra3	Nh4+
10.	Kc4+	Ka2	10.	Re6	Na7+	10.	Kf4+	Kh2
11.	Rg5	Nb2+	11.	Kd6	Kf8	11.	Ra5	Ng2+
12.	Kc3	Nd1+	12.	Kd7	Nb5	12.	Kf3	Ne1+
13.	Kc2	Ne3+	13.	Re3	Nd4	13.	Kf2	Nd3+
14.	Kd2	Nc4+	14.	Re4	Nb3	14.	Ke2	Nf4+
15.	Kc3	Ne3	15.	Kd6	Kg7	15.	Kf3	Nd3
16.	Re5	Ng4	16.	Kd5	Nd2	16.	Rd5	Nb4
17.	Re6	Kb1	17.	Rf4	Nb1	17.	Rd6	Kg1
18.	Kd2	Nf2	18.	Rf3	Kg6	18.	Ke2	Nc2
19.	Rb6+	Ka2	19.	Rd3	Kf5	19.	Rg6+	Kh2
20.	Rb4	Nh1	20.	Kc5	Ke4	20.	Rg4	Na1
21.	Rg4	Ka3	21.	Kc4	Ke5	21.	Rb4	Kh3
22.	Ke3	Kb3	22.	Kb4	Ke6	22.	Kd3	Kh2
23.	Rg1	'resigns'	23.	Rd1	'resigns'	23.	Rb1	'resigns'

I played with a clock (at the time-limit of 16 moves per hour) and I did not have any moves back. On the other hand, I had had over a week's notice of the positions, and naturally I prepared for the contest. In chess terms it was more like having an adjourned game.

I was already familiar, without being move-perfect, with what the books give on this ending. Also, I had learned a lot from playing against

R1   R2   R3

Three positions, all White to play. In all cases White captures the black knight
on his 24th move.

the same database at the April two-day conference in Edinburgh
(CW, May 25). Thirdly, I asked for, and was given in advance, four positions
(and the single-line optimal play) with the same solution length as the contest positions, so that I could have some training that was relevant (I refer
to these later as the Edinburgh lines).

The solutions were all 24 moves long, chosen at random from the 178
such positions, with the idea that the near-maximum length (no position
has an optimal solution exceeding 27 moves) and the number of such positions would provide the toughest and fairest contest conditions.

About five minutes was spent on each task. My preparation was pretty
good, and most of the difficult moves I had already written down. Not only
did I have notes, but an auxiliary board on which I moved the pieces around
when I wanted to before choosing the move to be played on the primary
board. This was all agreed in advance. But I used the auxiliary board seri-
ously only twice. The contest was between a chess analyst and a database,
not between an over-the-board master and a database, so the conditions
were deliberately made to ensure the analyst, myself, could not complain.

Coming to the play, the solution to R3 is very similar to that to R1,
a mirror image, or almost, from move 5 onwards. We were all surprised at
the lack of variety, certainly the apparent lack of variety, in the core of the
solutions. Even R2 was like one of the positions given to me in advance,
and the R1 and R3 lines were not new to me. But R1 and R2 are quite
distinct from each other.

The program might have diverged, by selecting an alternative equal
depth move at many possible branch-points, though it did not. But certainly,
most of the work was in the preparation, and a great deal of the play was
accidentally (not deliberately, anyway) to be found in the practice positions.

Speaking as an analyst, R2 is quite beautiful. And it will not be found
in the textbooks. Take the position after Black's third move (see R2.1).
The black knight and black king are striving to meet, to set up a standard
drawing set-up with both men next to each other on the edge. White has
to play very precisely to prevent this. In fact, I find the next 10 moves a
sheer delight.

Consider the position after 8 Rh7+ (see R2.2). Where can Black play

R2.1

R2.2

R4

his king? If he goes to e8 or to f8, the knight is immediately lost to a rook
check on h8. If he goes to g8, however, the rook plays to c7, winning the
knight by domination, since it has no safe squares. The same applies to the
move of Black's king to g6. So, in spite of the apparently wide choice,
Black really has only e6 and f6 to choose from. But even e6 fails to Rh6+
and the variety of ways in which the knight is now caught in just a few
more moves is quite delightful. So, really, only f6 will do for Black in R2.2.
The effect, in the mind, of comprehending each of these variations indi-
vidually, and all of the variations as a group, is strongly aesthetic.

After R1, R2 and R3 had been disposed of, I asked for three more
positions to be given to me without preparation. Here I would try to play
fast, but with up to three moves back — a kind of compromise between
over-the-board competitive play and how the analyst works. The result was
exactly the same. I made no mistakes (to everyone's surprise, including my
own) and it was remarkably easy. I assumed that the positions would trans-
pose into solutions that I already knew — indeed, into the essentially different R1 and R2 lines or into one of the Edinburgh lines. And they did.
An example is R4. It was not too difficult to find 1 Ke7 Kh6, 2 Kf6 Ne3,
3 Rg3 Nd5+, 4 Ke6 Nc7, 5 Kf5 Ne8, 6 Rg6+ Kh5, 7 Rc6 and we are in R1,
as near as makes no difference. I had no moves back in these three 'unseen'
positions. It turned out that all the moves I made were optimal. That is, no
moves I made prolonged the solution unnecessarily.

I tackled the contest by looking for patterns. For instance, the play
in all these long-solution positions seems to fall naturally into three phases.
In the first phase the chessmen are relatively dispersed, but Black must get
his king and knight together, or perpetually threaten to. At the end of this
we enter a second phase, the kernel of the struggle. where a sequence of a
dozen or so moves decides it, because eventually the knight is forced away
from its king. Phase three mops up the knight. Of course, mate threats
operate in any phase of the struggle, even in all phases.

Appendix 4. Benchmark of Twenty Positions

The following pages contain our benchmark of 20 positions which illustrate all the features of special difficulty for the knight's side of the ending of which we are aware. All positions are drawn with correct play.

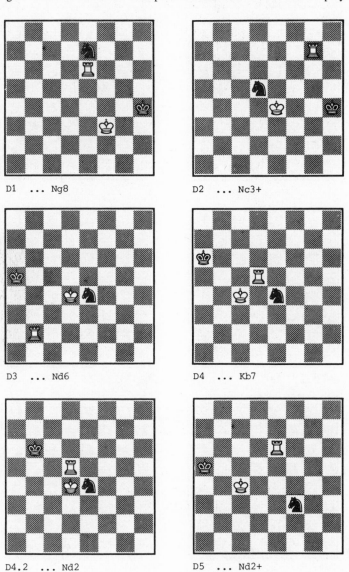

D1 ... Ng8

D2 ... Nc3+

D3 ... Nd6

D4 ... Kb7

D4.2 ... Nd2

D5 ... Nd2+

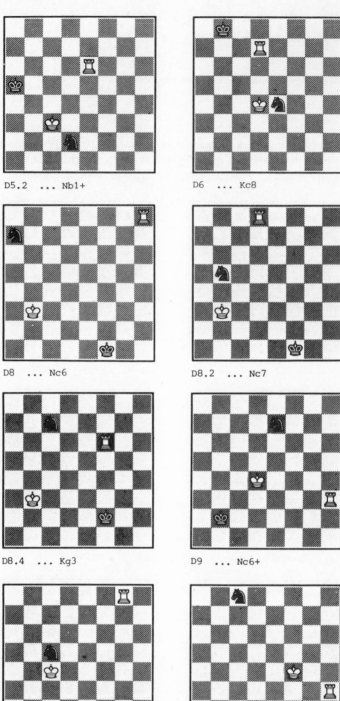

D5.2 ... Nb1+

D6 ... Kc8

D8 ... Nc6

D8.2 ... Nc7

D8.4 ... Kg3

D9 ... Nc6+

D10 ... Ne4

D12 ... Nb6
or Kc2 or Kd2 or Kb2

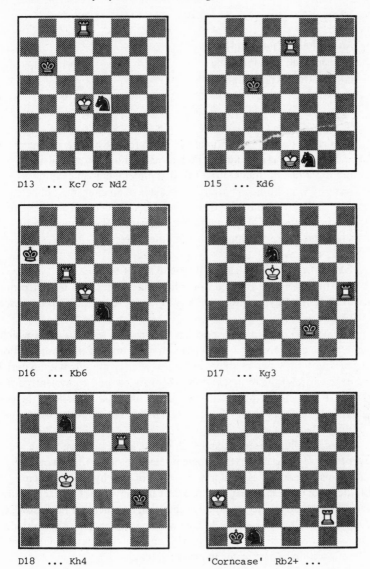

D13   ... Kc7 or Nd2

D15   ... Kd6

D16   ... Kb6

D17   ... Kg3

D18   ... Kh4

'Corncase'   Rb2+ ...

An Optimal Algorithm for
King and Pawn against King
using Pattern-Knowledge

M.A.Bramer

This paper presents an optimal algorithm for the basic endgame of king and one pawn against king (KPK), developed using the model and methods described in Bramer (1977b). It is presented as an example of the means by which human pattern-knowledge of an endgame can be represented and extended by use of the prescribed model, and as a basis for discussion of a number of general points concerning the application of Artificial Intelligence techniques to computer chess.

EVALUATING PROGRAM PERFORMANCE

A variety of terms are used in the literature to describe the performance of endgame-playing programs. The following terminology is proposed as standard.

Value-preserving. In every position the program selects a move which maintains the game-theoretic value (win, draw or loss) of the position. For endgames with only two possible outcomes (win for the side with material advantage or draw) the term *win-preserving* may be used equivalently for a program to find moves for the stronger side. This definition allows the possibility that the program may fail ever to win from some positions because of infinite repetition, etc.

Correct. Value-preserving and such that in every position where the player to move (P) can win, the program selects a move which would ultimately lead to victory against any sequence of play by the opponent, with the same program being used to select the moves for P at each future stage. Thus the possibility of infinite repetition or otherwise indecisive play is excluded but unnecessarily long winning sequences are permitted, as are programs which rely on recognizing and deliberately avoiding repetition of position as part of the winning strategy.

Optimal. Value-preserving and such that in every position where the player to move can win, the program selects a move which wins in the smallest possible number of ply. Notice that for convenience in making these definitions the fifty-move and three-fold repetition drawing rules are assumed not to apply. However, it is clear that for a program to be correct, it must always be able ultimately to break out of an infinite sequence of repetitions and for an optimal program no repetition of position with the same player to move can occur. These categories provide a framework by which the performance of endgame-playing programs can be evaluated.

In passing, it should be mentioned that certain tasks can be immediately dismissed as trivial, for example to write a value-preserving program for the stronger side in king and rook against king (KRK) or king and queen against king (KQK) (simply avoid stalemate and leaving the piece *en prise*) and to write an optimal program for the weaker side in those endgames (take the piece if possible, otherwise move at random). These elementary cases will not be considered further.

Databases currently exist containing the value of every position and, for won positions, the number of moves required to win for a variety of endgames including KPK, KRK, KQK, KQKR and KRKN.

Although the formats of the databases vary, in each case it is possible to find the move or moves that wins most rapidly in every won position and all other moves that 'preserve the win'. Thus in principle they can readily be used to validate either value-preserving or optimal play. So far, however, very few endgame-playing programs have been exhaustively tested against these databases, although some evidence of performance is available.

Beal (1977) gives a FORTRAN subroutine that contains 48 patterns used to classify each KPK position as either won for White or drawn, and this subroutine is fully validated as accurate against a KPK database. Such a subroutine can, of course, easily be used to construct a program which is provably win-preserving, although Beal also gives an algorithm that he believes may be correct.

Tan (1972) gives a program for KPK that is suggested as being value-preserving for both players (Tan uses the term 'correct'). However, a recent analysis (Bramer 1978) has shown this belief to be mistaken.

Neither Huberman's (1968) programs for KPK, king and two bishops against king, and king, bishop and knight against king, nor Zuidema's (1974) programs for KRK and KQK have been exhaustively tested, but in both cases the information and examples given show that the programs are not optimal.

No computationally feasible algorithm is currently known which would determine whether or not a given algorithm is correct by reference to a database. In this area the possibility of mathematical proofs of correctness cannot be discounted, however, and Michie (1978) reports such a proof by Bratko of an algorithm for KRK. It remains to be seen whether similar proofs can be found for other endgames. Formal program proving is, however, itself known as a particularly difficult problem. In the absence of either a feasible algorithm or a mathematical proof, use has been made of strong chess players to validate the correctness of an algorithm by practical tests.

Although interesting, such testing can logically refute but never prove correctness. In commercial programming it is commonly observed that a program that properly handles difficult test cases fails on much simpler ones. Practical experience also suggests that the area of chess endgame-playing programs is one in which intuition and judgement are often unreliable guides.

The KPK algorithm described below has been fully validated as optimal against a database. With the exception of programs that simply use a database as a huge look-up table, it is believed to be the only optimal endgame-playing program currently in existence.

There would, however, seem to be no reason why, using the same model and process of iterative refinement, optimal algorithms for other endgames could not also be developed.

THE PROGRAM

The structure of the program is based on the equivalence class model described in Bramer (1977b) and the program was developed by a continuation of the process of iterative refinement described there. For convenience the side with the pawn will be referred to as White throughout this paper. The program finds moves for White only, in all legal positions with the pawn on files a to d and ranks 2 to 7. Positions with the pawn on files e to h can, of course, be dealt with by a simple reflection about the centre line of the board. It is assumed that White wins immediately if the pawn reaches the eighth rank of the board and cannot immediately be captured (in some positions promoting to a queen will give stalemate, but White can always safely promote to a rook instead).

The procedure for selecting moves for White makes use of a partition of the set of legal positions with *Black* to move into a number of disjoint classes, each corresponding to some significant pattern of pieces to be achieved or avoided. Initially these patterns are derived from descriptions and examples in standard textbooks. Subsequently the patterns are modified or added to as the result of a continuing process of testing and refinement against either human opponents or (in this case) a database of perfect information about the endgame.

The classes are defined entirely statically with a fixed constant ranking amongst them. The positions within each class are ranked according to the values of a set of *associated functions* corresponding generally to geometrical distances, for example between two pieces. For ranking purposes, the functions are applied in order and the position with the largest or smallest value (as specified) is chosen. The second function is only used if the first is insufficient to discriminate between the positions and so on. After all the functions are exhausted the ranking is finally made by some (fixed) arbitrary criterion, such as the order in which the positions are generated. In each case where the program detects a tie, the positions genuinely are 'equal best' successors, as verified by the database.

The overall move finding algorithm is then as follows, for a given position with White to move.
(i)   Generate all legal successors (Black to move)
(ii)   Map each position to a corresponding class
(iii) Choose the successor position in the highest-ranked class. In the event of a tie, apply the associated functions successively in order until the tie is broken, using the order of move generation as the final tie-breaking criterion if necessary.

The mapping of positions to classes is made by a sequential search through an ordered set of rules with the first rule satisfied taken as specifying the class to which the position belongs. To ensure that all positions belong to some class, the final rule is defined as always *true*, corresponding to a 'residual' class of positions which satisfy none of the other rules.

A listing of an ALGOL 60 function procedure *findrow* is given in appendix 1. This takes the coordinates wkf, wkr, bkf, bkr, pf and pr corresponding to a position with Black to move as arguments and returns the number of a class as the value of the procedure. wkf and wkr represent the coordinates of the white king (e.g. for a king on square g3, wkf = 7, wkr = 3), and similarly for the black king and the pawn using White's bottom left-hand corner of the board as the origin of coordinates in all cases. The class number is used to reference a row of the *value table* given in appendix 2, which contains for each class the corresponding class value and the index numbers of each of its associated functions in order. A definition of the associated functions is also given in appendix 2. There are a total of 38 classes defined and 13 different associated functions, up to 4 of which are used with any given class. It will be seen that several of the classes have more than one component definition and in many cases these could be split into a number of separate classes if required. Equally, there are a number of instances where classes could be combined. The present composition is intended to reflect (approximately) a breakdown into separate 'ideas' as they might be seen by a chess player.

It is interesting to note in passing that the version of the program given in Bramer (1977b) contained only half as many classes (19) but was optimal in 96.6% of cases. Thus there is clearly a 'diminishing returns' effect as Beal's work bears out (the first seven of his forty-eight patterns are sufficient to classify over 70% of positions).

Further analysis of the algorithm might reveal possible reductions in the number of classes required or simplifications to their definitions. One promising approach to this would seem to be using the inductive procedures described by Michalski and Negri (1977).

Procedure *findrow* makes use of further (separate) procedures that determine statically whether Black is stalemated and whether the pawn can 'run', i.e. advance successively to the queening square without being blocked or captured by the opponent. Neither procedure is listed here, but a FORTRAN subroutine for the latter is given in Bramer (1977a). A further (external) procedure, *dist*, is used. This gives the 'block distance' between two squares, with coordinates i1, i2 and i3, i4 respectively. This is defined by

$$dist\ (i1, i2, i3, i4) = \text{maximum}\ (abs\ (i1 - i3), abs\ (i2 - i4)).$$

This is, in fact, the number of 'king moves' needed to move from one square to the other.

Use is also made of prr, the 'effective rank' of the pawn. This is equal to pr except when pr = 2 in which case prr = 3. The effective rank is particularly useful when constructing the queening square of the pawn.

The program uses no tree-searching at all below the level of the immediate successors of the given position. In this relatively simple case, the absence of search makes the program a suitable vehicle for studies of automatic methods of inductive refinement. For more difficult endgames, a balance inevitably may need to be found between using pattern-knowledge and analysis. The means by which analysis can be incorporated into the model in a readily controllable fashion are discussed in Bramer (1977b).

An approach based where possible solely on pattern matching does, however, have the additional advantage of making more explicit the underlying principles of the endgames concerned.

HOW HARD IS OPTIMAL KPK?

The standard endgame works by Fine (1941), and Averbakh and Maizelis (1974) devote approximately 2 and 6 pages respectively to KPK. Using only the information explicitly given in these texts, it is unlikely that a beginner (who knew only the legal moves and laws of chess) would be able to play even a value-preserving game. For a more experienced player (the 'practitioner') the information in the text conveys a great deal more meaning derived from some generalization of the specific examples given and an appreciation of the limitations of general rules. It may be said that the experienced reader possesses an overall 'conceptual framework' in terms of which the rules and examples in the text book are interpreted. It is this framework which the model described above is designed to represent.

Even allowing for this improved level of interpretation it is commonly observed that many competent players at club level in Britain do not play win-preserving KPK, even when they are familiar with standard texts. This may partly be explained by the fact that, in many cases, important examples are omitted from textbooks. For examples, Fine does not give (although Averbakh and Maizelis do) the well-known position WK:d1, BK:f8, WP:c3 in which White to move wins in 27 ply by 1 Kc2!, all other moves drawing. This is a clear example of a position in which pattern-knowledge rather than analytical skill is required in practical play.

At a higher level of chess skill, it is often suggested that expert players perform optimally at KPK. However, a recent experiment suggests that this is not always so. In this a number of players, of whom the strongest was a U.S master (U.S.C.F rating 2342), were sent a sample of 33 KPK positions and asked to give the best (in the sense of 'optimal') move (or all equal best moves) for White, the side with the pawn. Surprisingly, the master chose a non-optimal move in 4 cases, in two other cases missed equally good alternatives and in two cases gave alternative 'best' moves where only one move was optimal. In one of the latter cases, a move was given as 'equal best' which in fact was not even win-preserving. Further details are given in Bramer (1978). This result suggests that KPK may not be as completely understood by chess players as is often believed. It seems probable that in practical endgame play chess players make considerable use of pattern knowledge, relying on analysis to supplement this in difficult cases. Non-optimal play will then naturally occur either when there is no apparent reason to suppose that a position is a 'difficult case' or where the analysis is too lengthy to perform accurately. The need to find optimal rather than correct winning sequences is one which virtually never occurs in practical play, so the sophisticated pattern-knowledge needed to play

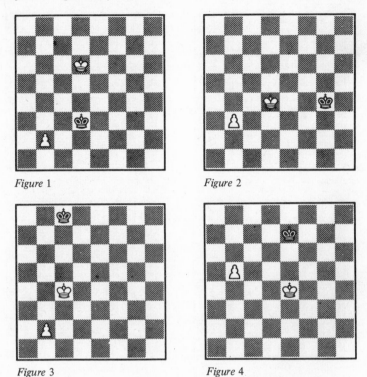

Figure 1

Figure 2

Figure 3

Figure 4

optimally need never be acquired. For KPK there are many cases where it is necessary to recognize positions where the pawn can 'run'. The majority of these are obvious from a cursory inspection but there are some which can occur unexpectedly.

Thus, in figure 1, White should play not 1 Kc5 but 1 Kd5, allowing the pawn to run. 1 Kc5 is sub-optimal, since Black could now catch the pawn via e4, e5, e6, d7 and c7, a sequence highly unlikely to arise in practical play. In figure 2, White should play 1 Ke5, when again the pawn runs. This and the above example seem quite difficult to perceive, possibly because they run counter to the intuitive idea that White should keep his king on the files near the pawn where possible.

In other positions White is faced by an excess of good alternatives. For example, in figure 3 it is not clear whether 1 Kb5 or 1 Kc5 is the stronger move. In fact, the optimal move is 1 Kb5, blocking the advance of the pawn. (Note that 1 b4 fails to 1 ... Kb8! drawing.) In figure 4, White should play 1 Kd5 allowing Black to take the opposition and if 1 ... Kd7, 2 b6! Taking the opposition by 1 Ke5 only draws. In figure 5, White's quickest winning move is 1 Ke6 not 1 Kf6, again rejecting the opportunity to take the opposition, although the latter move also wins.

Particular difficulties occur where the normal apparent 'invariance' to shifting all the pieces one or more files to the right or left (or one or more ranks up or down the board) does not hold. In figure 6, both 1 Kb4 and 1 Kc4 are equally good, either winning in 19 ply. However if all the pieces

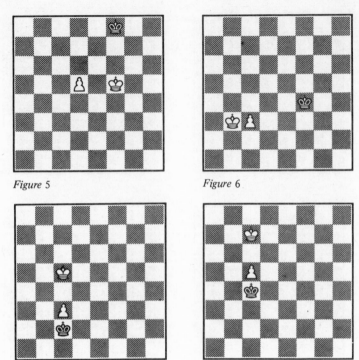

Figure 5   Figure 6

Figure 7   Figure 8

are now moved one file to the right, the situation is changed. The optimal
play is now to move the king one square forward. The previous alternative
of moving the king in front of the pawn is now no longer equally good!
It is safe to say that this strange situation is not given in endgame textbooks
and does not form part of the chess player's knowledge of KPK. Nor is it
likely that most chess players would anticipate that there would be any
difference between the two cases. The underlying reason is, in fact, the
possibility of stalemate with the black king on a8 and the pawn on c7,
many moves further on.

As a final example, figure 7 introduces a complicated family of positions. Here White should play 1 Kc4! (winning in 13 ply). If 1 Kb4, Kd3
and White wins in a total of 19 ply. If 1 c4, Kc3! and White wins in a total
of 15 ply. If now the pieces in figure 7 are all moved down one rank, White's
best moves are 1 Kb3 or 1 Kd3, and in either case the pawn runs (winning
in 11 ply total, two ply *fewer* than figure 7). If the pieces in figure 7 are
moved up one rank instead, either 1 Kc5 or 1 c5 wins in 11 ply. Moving
the pieces up one further rank to figure 8, 1 c6 is now the sole optimal
move (7 ply). Moving up an additional rank, there are now four optimal
moves: 1 Kb7, 1 Kc7, 1 Kd7, and 1 c7. The reader may care to examine
for himself the equivalent positions with the pawn on the rook and knight
files, in both of which cases the outcome may be subject to board edge
effects.

In view of the myriad difficult examples and special cases for this apparently well-understood endgame (of which the above are only a small selection) it is perhaps not surprising that endgame-playing programs based on a procedural (as opposed to a structural) approach inevitably seem to become complex and hard to modify. Nor is it surprising that, as mentioned earlier, Beal's subroutine for discriminating KPK wins from draws contains 48 fairly complex rules, and it would seem that this number is unlikely to be significantly reduced in the future.

RELATIONSHIP TO THE AIMS OF
ARTIFICIAL INTELLIGENCE RESEARCH

The majority of research into endgame-playing programs at the present time is orientated towards an Artificial Intelligence-like view of the problem. Thus the principal emphasis is on developing methods and techniques of knowledge representation that may prove generalizable to other problems in chess and ultimately elsewhere, rather than on algorithms to perform deep analysis, which it is widely recognized will not prove feasible for the more complex endgames (even for KPK, searches of 37 ply would be needed for White in the most extreme cases).

Assuming that chess players play most endgames (and perhaps all end-games) at best correctly, not optimally, the researcher faces a dilemma: whether to attempt an implementation of the chess player's knowledge in the form of a correct algorithm or to aim to go beyond this for an optimal playing strategy. The former is likely to be easier to construct and may more closely mirror human playing strategies but in general may be extremely difficult to validate formally. The latter although difficult to construct may be much easier to validate, and provided that a largely pattern-based approach is adopted and that difficult cases are dealt with where possible by the (possibly machine-aided) synthesis of new rules, rather than the proliferation of numerous specific 'special cases', this approach is likely to lead to new subject knowledge that has the advantage of being provable as correct by automatic methods. Programs that combine relatively little knowledge with deep analysis to play optimally are, of course, much less likely to be valuable in this respect.

These considerations are particularly relevant in the context of an analysis by Michie (1978) of what properly constitutes objectives for Artificial Intelligence research. He stresses the need for Artificial Intelligence techniques to be complementary to (not in competition with) conventional algorithmic methods and lays strong emphasis on the development of *conceptual interfaces* (so that the content of high-performance programs can be expressed in a form meaningful to human experts) and on the aim of *knowledge enhancement* so that new results obtained during the construction and development of a program can be fed back as new theoretical knowledge in the subject area.

The optimal algorithm given here consists of pattern-knowledge acquired by a process of iterative refinement based on exception reporting against the optimal moves derived from a database. It would be a straightforward matter to implement an advice-taking system where new patterns and associated functions were supplied by expert chess players in a convenient and interactive fashion. The final program incorporates new pattern-knowledge that, although easily justifiable empirically by reference to the database, would have been virtually impossible to prove rigorously, or even to find, by non-automatic methods. Thus for example, class 8 with the value given is all the additional information that is needed to deal with the complications of the family of positions related to figure 7 above. The development of the program has prompted the mathematical analysis of the 'effective distance' between two squares (i.e. the shortest distance between them measured in king moves, subject to an area of inaccessible squares of the board) which is embedded in the 'pawn can run' subroutine. This subroutine correctly classifies all of the 36959 such positions with Black to move (and no others), in the state space of 84012 positions with Black to move and the pawn on files a-d, ranks 2-7. Moreover, the form of a number of the rules in the program prompts conjectures that are then readily verifiable against the database, as extensions to the existing theoretical understanding of the endgame. The following theorems all apply to positions with Black to move and take the 'block distance' defined previously as the measure of distance.

Theorem 1. In any position where Black can legally move to the 'blockade square' (the square in front of the pawn) the game is drawn. The drawing method is simply to occupy the blockade square except when the pawn can immediately be taken.

Theorems 2-4 apply only to positions where the black king is no more than one rank or file outside the queening square.

Theorem 2. In any position in which the black king is closer to the blockade square than the white king (but does not occupy it when the pawn is on the seventh rank) the game is drawn. For this purpose the calculation of the black king's distance must be increased by one if the black king and the pawn are both on the second rank and two files apart.

Theorem 3. In any position where the black king is closer to the 'reserve blockade square' (the square two in front of the pawn) than the white king, the pawn is below the sixth rank and the black king is above the rank of the pawn, the game is drawn.

Theorem 4. In any position where the black king is closer to the pawn than the white king as defined below, and the pawn is above the second rank the game is drawn.

The black king's distance from the pawn must be less than the white king's, where the former measurement (for this purpose only) is increased by one if the black king is diagonally ahead of the pawn and more than one square away from it (since then a one-move detour will be required to reach the pawn).

Theorem 5. In any position where the pawn is on the a-file and the black king is closer to square c8 than the white king, the game is drawn, excluding cases where the pawn can run.

In the state space of 84012 legal positions with Black to move, 48802 are wins for White and 35210 are draws.

Theorems 1-5 correctly classify 7267, 25462, 16144, 18558 and 6303 of these positions as draws, with theorems 1-5 together accounting for 31308 positions. (Strictly Theorems 1 and 2 each have six exceptions, similar to the following WK:b6, BK:a8, WP:b7. Although these positions are legal, they have no legal antecedents (except from a pawn capture) in the state space. If required these could, of course, easily be excluded from the theorems.)

Future investigations will concentrate on developing algorithms for more complex endgames by the methods illustrated here. It is to be hoped that this will lead to further extensions of existing theoretical knowledge of the endgame.

REFERENCES

Averbakh, Y. & I. Maizelis (1974) *Pawn Endings*. London: Batsford.

Beal, D.F. (1977) *Discriminating wins from draws in king and pawn versus king chess endgames*. Queen Mary College, London, Department of Computer Science and Statistics.

Bramer, M.A. (1977a) *King and pawn against king: using effective distance*. Open University, Faculty of Mathematics, Technical Report.

Bramer, M.A. (1977b) *Representation of knowledge for chess endgames: towards a self-improving system*. Ph.D. thesis, Open University.

Bramer, M.A. (1978) *A note on king and pawn against king*. Open University, Faculty of Mathematics, Technical Report.

Fine, R. (1941) *Basic chess endings*. New York: David McKay.

Huberman, B.J. (1968) *A program to play chess endgames*. Ph.D. dissertation, Stanford University.

Michalski, R.S. & P. Negri (1977) An experiment on inductive learning in chess endgames, in *Machine Intelligence 8* (eds. E.W.Elcock & D.Michie) pp. 175-92. Chichester: Ellis Horwood.

Michie, D. (1978) New face of artificial intelligence. *AISB Quarterly 29*, 14-18.

Tan, S.T. (1972) *Representation of knowledge for very simple pawn endings in chess*. University of Edinburgh, School of Artificial Intelligence, Memorandum MIP-R-98.

Zuidema, C. (1974) Chess, *How to Program the Exceptions?* Stichting Mathematisch Centrum, Ze Boerhaavestraat 49 Amsterdam.

Appendix 1. Listing of Procedure 'Findrow'

```
INTEGER PROCEDURE findrow(wkf,wkr,bkf,bkr,pf,pr);
    VALUE wkf,wkr,bkf,bkr,pf,pr; INTEGER wkf,wkr,bkf,bkr,pf,pr;
BEGIN
    BOOLEAN PROCEDURE bknext(file,rank);
    VALUE file,rank; INTEGER file,rank;
    bknext:= IF dist(bkf,bkr,file,rank)=1 THEN true ELSE false;
    BOOLEAN PROCEDURE bknearer(file,rank);
    VALUE file,rank; INTEGER file,rank;
    bknearer:= IF dist(bkf,bkr,file,rank)<dist(wkf,wkr,file,rank)
    THEN true ELSE false;
    INTEGER prr,dwkp,dbkp,dwkbk,wkint,bkint,bkinc;
    BOOLEAN rpawn,oppside,between;
    bkinc:= IF abs(bkf-pf)=bkr-pr AND bkr>pr+1 THEN 1 ELSE 0;
    IF pr=2 THEN prr:=3 ELSE prr:=pr;
    wkint:=wkr-pr-abs(wkf-pf);bkint:=bkr-pr-abs(bkf-pf);
    rpawn:=IF pf=1 THEN true ELSE false;
    oppside:=IF sign(wkf-pf)=sign(pf-bkf) THEN true ELSE false;
    between:=IF sign(bkf-wkf)=sign(wkf-pf) THEN true ELSE false;
    dwkp:=abs(wkf-pf);dbkp:=abs(bkf-pf);dwkbk:=abs(wkf-bkf);
findrow:=
        IF dist(bkf,bkr,pf,pr)=1 AND dist(wkf,wkr,pf,pr)>1 THEN 1
ELSE IF stalemate(wkf,wkr,bkf,bkr,pf,pr) THEN 2
ELSE IF pr=8 THEN 3
ELSE IF canrun(wkf,wkr,bkf,bkr,pf,pr) THEN 4
ELSE IF dist(wkf,wkr,pf,pr)>dist(bkf,bkr,pf,pr)+bkinc
        AND (pr>2 OR bknearer(pf,3))
        AND bkr>=prr-1 THEN 5
ELSE IF wkf=bkf AND wkr=6 AND bkr=3 AND dwkp=2
        AND pr=4 THEN 5
ELSE IF bknearer(pf,pr+1) AND NOT (bkf=pf AND bkr=pr+1) THEN 5
ELSE IF bknearer(pf,pr+2) AND bkr>pr AND pr<6 THEN 5
ELSE IF oppside AND bkr>pr AND wkr>pr
        AND ((wkint=0 AND bkint=0 AND wkr=bkr+1)
        OR (dist(wkf,wkr,pf,pr)=dist(bkf,bkr,pf,pr)
        AND bkint>0 AND wkint<bkint)) THEN 6
ELSE IF rpawn AND wkf=pf AND wkr>pr AND bknext(3,wkr) THEN 7
ELSE IF rpawn AND bknearer(3,8) THEN 7
ELSE IF rpawn AND wkf=pf AND wkr>=pr+2
        AND bknext(3,wkr-1) THEN 7
ELSE IF rpawn AND pr>2 AND wkr=pr+4
        AND bknext(3,pr+2) THEN 7
ELSE IF rpawn AND wkf=pf AND wkr=pr+1
        AND bknext(3,wkr+1) THEN 7
ELSE IF rpawn AND wkf=pf AND wkr=pr+3
        AND bknext(3,wkr-2) THEN 7
ELSE IF wkf=pf AND bkf=pf AND pr=3 AND bkr=2
        AND wkr=4 THEN 8
ELSE IF dbkp=4 AND (dwkp=2 OR dwkp=3) AND oppside
        AND wkr=8 AND ((bkr>6 AND pr=3) OR (bkr=8 AND pr=2))
        THEN 9
ELSE IF pr>bkr AND wkr>=bkr AND dbkp<=3 THEN 10
```

```
ELSE IF dbkp=3 AND pr=4 AND bkr=4
        AND wkr>=bkr AND dwkp=1 AND oppside THEN 10
ELSE IF dbkp=3 AND pr=4 AND (bkr=5 OR bkr=6)
        AND dwkp=1 AND oppside AND (wkr=4 OR wkr=5) THEN 10
ELSE IF dbkp=3 AND pr=5 AND (bkr=5 OR bkr=6)
        AND oppside AND wkr>4 THEN 10
ELSE IF between AND dwkbk=2 AND wkr=bkr
        AND pr<=wkr AND pr>=4 THEN 10
ELSE IF dbkp=3 AND wkf=pf AND wkr>pr AND bkr<5 THEN 11
ELSE IF dwkp>=3 AND dbkp=5
        AND between AND pr<4 AND wkr>6 THEN 12
ELSE IF dbkp=3 AND dwkbk>2 AND bkr>4
        AND (oppside OR between OR wkf=pf)
        AND ((bkr=5 AND wkr>=5) OR (bkr=6 AND wkr>=5)
        OR (bkr=8 AND wkr>=7) OR (bkr>5 AND wkr>=6))
        AND NOT (wkf=pf AND pr<4 AND bkr<7 AND wkr<7)
        AND NOT (dwkp=1 AND pr<4 AND wkr=5 AND (bkr=5 OR bkr=6))
        THEN 13
ELSE IF dbkp>2 AND dwkbk>1
        AND wkr>=pr AND (oppside OR between OR wkf=pf)
        AND NOT (dbkp>3 AND dwkbk=2 AND bkr>4) THEN 14
ELSE IF bknext(wkf,wkr+2) AND wkr<pr+2
        AND NOT ((pr=6 AND wkr=5) OR (pr=5 AND wkr=6)
        OR (pr=5 AND wkr=5 AND dwkp>1)
        OR (pr=wkr+1 AND abs(wkf-pf)=1)) THEN 15
ELSE IF pf=2 AND bkf=1 AND bkr=8
        AND ((wkf=3 AND wkr=7) OR (wkf=2 AND wkr=6))
        AND pr<wkr THEN 16
ELSE IF pf=2 AND bkf=1 AND bkr=7 AND wkf=3
        AND (wkr=6 OR wkr=7) AND pr=5 THEN 16
ELSE IF pf=2 AND bkf=1 AND bkr=7 AND wkf=3
        AND (wkr=6 OR wkr=7) AND pr=4 THEN 17
ELSE IF bknext(wkf,wkr+2) AND wkf=pf AND wkr=pr+1 THEN 18
ELSE IF dwkp>2 AND wkr>pr AND oppside THEN 19
ELSE IF wkr=bkr AND dwkp=dbkp
        AND oppside AND bkr>prr+3 THEN 20
ELSE IF wkr=bkr AND dwkp=dbkp-1
        AND oppside AND bkr>prr+2 THEN 20
ELSE IF dbkp=2 AND dwkp<=1 AND bkr=7 AND pr=5
        AND wkr>5 THEN 21
ELSE IF wkf=pf AND pr<5 AND dbkp=2 AND bkr>6
        AND (wkr=6 OR (wkr=7 AND bkr=8)) THEN 22
ELSE IF wkf=pf AND dbkp=2
        AND ((wkr>6 AND wkr=bkr AND pr=4)
        OR (wkr>=6 AND bkr=7 AND pr=5)) THEN 22
ELSE IF dwkbk=1 AND dbkp=2 AND between AND wkr=bkr+2
        AND ((pr=2 AND bkr=3) OR (pr=2 AND bkr=2)
        OR (pr=3 AND bkr=3)) THEN 23
ELSE IF dbkp=2 AND dwkp=1 AND oppside
        AND bkr=pr+1 AND wkr=pr+2 AND (pr=2 OR pr=4)
        THEN 23
ELSE IF dbkp=2 AND pr=5 AND bkr=5
        AND wkf=pf AND wkr>pr THEN 24
ELSE IF  bkr>3 AND dbkp=2 AND wkf=pf
        AND wkr>4 AND pr<7 AND wkr>pr THEN 25
ELSE IF bkr>3 AND dbkp=2
        AND dwkp=1 AND oppside AND pr<7 AND wkr>=pr
        AND ((pr=4 AND (wkr>=bkr OR (wkr=5 AND bkr=6)
        OR (wkr=5 AND bkr=8) OR (wkr=6 AND bkr>6)))
        OR (pr=5 AND wkr=5 AND bkr=5)
        OR (pr=5 AND wkr>5 AND bkr>4) OR (wkr>=5 AND pr<4))
        AND NOT (wkr=5 AND bkr>6 AND pr=3) THEN 25
```

```
ELSE IF bkr>3 AND dbkp=2 AND dwkp=2 AND oppside AND pr<7
        AND (pr=4 OR pr=5) AND wkr>pr THEN 25
ELSE IF dwkbk>=2 AND (between OR wkf=pf)
        AND wkr>pr THEN 26
ELSE IF dbkp>=2 AND (oppside OR pf=wkf) AND wkr>pr THEN 26
ELSE IF dwkp=1 AND dbkp=2 AND between AND wkr=6
        AND bkr=8 AND pr=5 AND NOT (pf=3 AND bkf=1)
        THEN 27
ELSE IF wkf=1 AND bkf=1 AND pf=2
        AND wkr=6 AND bkr=8 AND (pr=4 OR pr=6) THEN 28
ELSE IF wkr=6 AND bkr=8 AND dwkp<=1
        AND NOT (wkf=3 AND bkf=2 AND pf=2
        AND wkr=6 AND bkr=8 AND pr=5) THEN 29
ELSE IF wkr>=bkr AND oppside AND dwkp=1
        AND wkr<prr+3 AND dbkp=1 THEN 30
ELSE IF wkr>pr AND wkr<=prr+3 AND
        dwkp=1 AND dbkp=1 AND bkr=wkr+1 THEN 31
ELSE IF wkf=bkf AND bkr=wkr+2 AND wkr>pr AND dwkp<2
        AND wkf≠pf THEN 32
ELSE IF wkf=pf AND wkr>pr THEN 33
ELSE IF dwkp<2 AND wkr>pr AND wkr<=prr+3 THEN 34
ELSE IF wkr>pr AND wkr<bkr-1 THEN 35
ELSE IF wkr=pr AND wkr=5 AND bkr=7
        AND dwkp=2 AND dbkp=3 AND between THEN 36
ELSE IF wkf=bkf AND dwkp=2 AND wkr=pr AND wkr=6 AND bkr=8
        AND NOT (pf=3 AND bkf=1) THEN 37
ELSE 38;
END;
```

Appendix 2. Value Table for Optimal KPK Algorithm

Class	Class Value	Associated Functions			
		1st	2nd	3rd	4th
1	1	2	3	-	-
2	2	-	-	-	-
3	38	-	-	-	-
4	37	1	-	-	-
5	3	2	3	-	-
6	5	-	-	-	-
7	4	-	-	-	-
8	36	-	-	-	-
9	7	-	-	-	-
10	35	1	7	11	13
11	9	-	-	-	-
12	27	8	4	-	-
13	34	1	7	11	-
14	31	7	1	11	-
15	6	-	-	-	-
16	23	1	11	12	-
17	22	7	-	-	-
18	8	-	-	-	-
19	10	4	8	-	-
20	11	-	-	-	-
21	30	5	-	-	-
22	28	1	7	-	-
23	32	7	-	-	-
24	33	-	-	-	-
25	26	1	7	4	-
26	25	4	7	-	-
27	29	-	-	-	-
28	24	-	-	-	-
29	21	1	4	9	13
30	20	1	7	-	-
31	19	1	-	-	-
32	16	-	-	-	-
33	18	7	1	-	-
34	15	1	6	-	-
35	14	4	10	-	-
36	17	-	-	-	-
37	13	-	-	-	-
38	12	2	3	7	9

Associated Functions

Index	Definition	Max or Min
1	pr	Max
2	*dist*(wkf, wkr, pf, pr)	Min
3	minimum (*abs*(wkf − pf), *abs*(wkr − pr))	Min
4	*abs*(wkf − pf)	Min
5	*abs*(wkf − pf)	Max
6	wkr − pr	Max
7	wkr	Max
8	*abs*(wkr − pr)	Min
9	*abs*(wkf − bkf)	Max
10	*abs*(wkr − bkr)	Min
11	*abs*(wkf − bkf)	Min
12	wkr	Min
13	wkf	Max

Kings and Pawns :
The Theory of Coordinate Squares

M.R.B.Clarke

Averbakh and Maizelis in their comprehensive book 'Pawn Endings', henceforth referred to as AM, discuss a number of related concepts under the names of key squares, related squares, coordinate squares, and the opposition.

Key or critical squares are those which if occupied by White, assuming him to be the attacking side, enable him to win immediately, whereas if Black can permanently prevent White from occupying them he is able to defend. A particularly simple example is afforded by endings with a single pawn, discussed in another paper in this book, where the opposition is a tactical device by which one side forces the other to abandon control of one of a system of three key squares. The concept of coordinate squares is more general but not so precisely defined.

Figure 1. b5 and a7 are
coordinate squares

Figure 2. E.Lasker (1901)
White to play and win

In figure 1 for example, each king would like to occupy a key square immediately after his opponent. Accomplishing this forces the opponent to abandon his pawn. For White the key square is b5, for Black a7, so with White to move the best play is 1 Kb4 Ka8, 2 Kc4 Kb8, 3 Kb4 Ka8 with a draw the result; variation by either side would clearly lose.

In this simple case because of the maoeuvrability of the kings there is no coordinate relationship between squares to the rear but for more complex examples there may be. To illustrate this I use (figure 2) a famous study by Lasker (AM 671). The key squares are b5 and g5 because if White is allowed to move to either he wins at once. But a direct attack by White on either fails because Black can get there in time to defend. For example 1 Kb3 Kb7, 2 Kc4 Kb6, 3 Kd3 Kc7 4 Ke3 Kd7, 5 Kf3 Ke7, 6 Kg3 Kf6, 7 Kh4 Kg6.

Nevertheless the position is a win for White because he has the possibility of moving in such a way as to catch Black in *Zugzwang* and force him to abandon the narrow path from which he can defend both key squares. The solution is the counter-intuitive 1 Kb2 Ka7, 2 Kb3 Kb7, 3 Kc3 Kc7, 4 Kd3 and now if 4 ... Kd7, 5 Kc4 etc., or if 4 ... Kb6 5 Ke3 etc., or if earlier 2 ... Ka6 3 Kc2.

This solution (and many others in similar endings) is 'deduced' in AM by a complicated method of labelling the coordinate squares with numbers and letters. In general this theory seems not to be capable of precise definition and in some cases to owe as much to art as science. The purpose of this paper is to show how problems of this type can be solved by the same method of deduction based on backing-up that we have used in simpler endings.

METHOD

The first step is to label each square for which the information is relevant with its minimum-path distance from each of the two key squares (figure 3). Naturally in doing this one must take account of squares made inaccessible by enemy pawns. In the case of the Lasker study, with reservations discussed later, we omit for simplicity consideration of lines where White and Black simultaneously penetrate each other's pawn chains. There are thus 26 squares to be considered for the white king and 21 for Black, the complete state space for this problem, where the pawn chain is static, consisting of only 26 × 21 = 546 configurations.

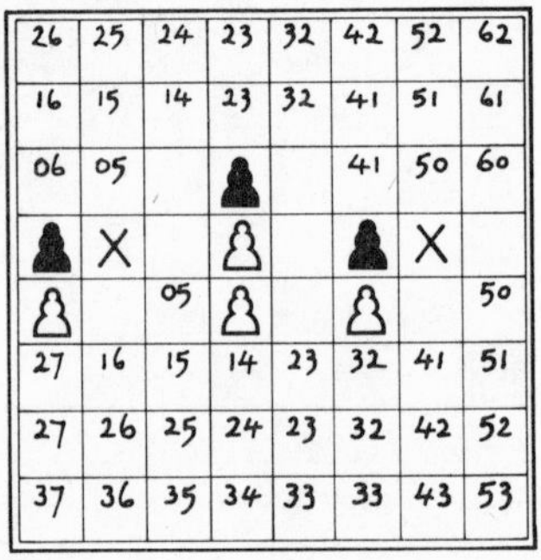

Figure 3. Distances for the Lasker study

The procedure is now to evaluate the position corresponding to these 546 king-square pairs by backing-up as described in Clarke (1977). Assuming that White either wins or draws, we say that a position is a terminal, depth 1, win for White if on the move he is nearer one or other of the critical squares. That is if $W_1 < B_1$ or $W_r < B_r$ where W_1, W_r are the White minimum path distances from the left- and right-hand critical squares and similarly for Black. WK on d3, BK on d7 is a pair satisfying this criterion. Having marked these points of the state space as depth 1 wins for White we then back up and label all positions in which Black cannot avoid moving to one of the White wins as depth 1 losses for Black. Depth 2 wins for White are then those positions in which he can move to a depth 1 Black loss, and so the process continues until no more positions can be evaluated.

W\B	a6	b6	f6	g6	h6	a7	b7	c7	d7	e7	f7	g7	h7	a8	b8	c8	d8	e8	f8	g8	h8
a1	60	60	14	11	11	80	0	80	0	40	14	11	11	60	0	60	0	40	14	11	11
b1	40	40	14	11	11	7	70	7	50	45	14	11	11	60	50	60	50	45	14	11	11
c1	10	30	14	11	11	10	6	60	56	45	14	11	11	10	50	40	56	45	14	11	11
d1	11	10	14	11	11	11	10	5	50	45	14	11	11	11	10	40	50	45	14	11	11
e1	11	11	14	11	11	11	11	10	0	40	14	11	11	11	11	10	0	40	14	11	11
f1	11	11	10	11	11	11	11	10	0	0	10	11	11	11	11	10	0	0	10	11	11
g1	11	11	0	10	11	11	11	10	0	0	0	10	11	11	11	10	0	0	0	10	11
h1	11	11	0	0	10	11	11	10	0	0	0	0	10	11	11	10	0	0	0	0	10
a2	60	60	11	11	11	50	0	40	0	10	11	11	11	60	0	60	0	10	11	11	11
b2	45	45	11	11	11	50	30	40	30	13	11	11	11	5	50	5	30	13	11	11	11
c2	13	33	11	11	11	10	30	20	34	13	11	11	11	10	4	40	34	13	11	11	11
d2	11	12	11	11	11	11	10	20	30	13	11	11	11	11	10	3	30	13	11	11	11
e2	11	11	11	11	11	11	11	10	0	10	11	11	11	11	11	10	0	10	11	11	11
f2	11	11	10	11	11	11	11	11	10	0	10	11	11	11	11	11	10	0	10	11	11
g2	11	11	0	10	11	11	11	11	10	0	0	10	11	11	11	11	10	0	0	10	11
h2	11	11	0	0	10	11	11	11	10	0	0	0	10	11	11	11	10	0	0	0	10
a3	60	60	11	11	11	50	0	40	0	10	11	11	11	60	0	60	0	10	11	11	11
b3	40	20	11	11	11	4	30	3	10	11	11	11	11	10	10	10	10	11	11	11	11
c3	10	20	11	11	11	10	2	20	12	11	11	11	11	10	10	10	12	11	11	11	11
d3	11	10	11	11	11	11	10	1	10	11	11	11	11	10	10	10	11	11	11	11	11
e3	11	11	11	11	11	11	11	10	0	10	11	11	11	11	11	10	0	10	11	11	11
f3	11	11	10	11	11	11	11	11	10	0	10	11	11	11	11	11	10	0	10	11	11
g3	11	11	0	10	11	11	11	11	11	10	0	10	11	11	11	11	11	10	10	10	11
h3	11	11	0	20	10	11	11	11	11	10	0	0	10	11	11	11	11	10	10	10	10
c4	10	1	11	11	11	10	10	10	11	11	11	11	11	11	11	11	11	11	11	11	11
h4	11	11	10	1	10	11	11	11	11	11	10	10	10	11	11	11	11	11	11	11	11

Figure 4. The backed-up evaluation of every configuration in the complete state space for the Lasker study

Figure 4 shows an inventory of the state space at this stage with black king positions listed across the top and White down the left-hand side of the table. The two-digit figures in the body of the table represent the values of the corresponding state space configuration with White, the left-hand figure, and Black, the right-hand, to move respectively; zeros indicating unevaluated and hence drawn positions. Thus an entry 40 indicates that White to move has a win in 4 moves whereas Black to move can draw, and the winning line for White can be found by examining the values of adjacent squares.

To solve the Lasker study we find the entry corresponding to the initial configurations WK on a3, BK on a8, which is 60, indicating that this is a win for White in 6 moves whereas if it was Black to move he could draw.

W\B	a6	b6	f6	g6	h6	a7	b7	c7	d7	e7	f7	g7	h7	a8	b8	c8	d8	e8	f8	g8	h8
a1	63	63	0	0	0	85	0	85	0	43	0	0	0	63	0	63	0	43	0	0	0
b1	43	43	0	0	0	0	75	0	53	0	0	0	0	62	53	62	53	0	0	0	0
c1	0	33	0	0	0	0	0	65	52	0	0	0	0	0	52	43	52	0	0	0	0
d1	0	0	0	0	0	0	0	0	0	51	0	0	0	0	0	0	42	51	0	0	0
e1	0	0	0	0	0	0	0	0	0	41	0	0	0	0	0	0	0	41	0	0	0
f1	0	0	0	0	0	0	0	0	0	0	0	0	0	0	0	0	0	0	0	0	0
g1	0	0	0	0	0	0	0	0	0	0	0	0	0	0	0	0	0	0	0	0	0
h1	0	0	0	0	0	0	0	0	0	0	0	0	0	0	0	0	0	0	0	0	0
a2	65	65	0	0	0	53	0	43	0	0	0	0	0	65	0	65	0	0	0	0	0
b2	45	45	0	0	0	52	33	42	33	0	0	0	0	0	55	0	33	0	0	0	0
c2	0	35	0	0	0	0	32	23	32	0	0	0	0	0	0	45	32	0	0	0	0
d2	0	0	0	0	0	0	0	22	31	0	0	0	0	0	0	0	31	0	0	0	0
e2	0	0	0	0	0	0	0	0	0	0	0	0	0	0	0	0	0	0	0	0	0
f2	0	0	0	0	0	0	0	0	0	0	0	0	0	0	0	0	0	0	0	0	0
g2	0	0	0	0	0	0	0	0	0	0	0	0	0	0	0	0	0	0	0	0	0
h2	0	0	0	0	0	0	0	0	0	0	0	0	0	0	0	0	0	0	0	0	0
a3	68	68	0	0	0	55	0	45	0	0	0	0	0	68	0	68	0	0	0	0	0
b3	48	23	0	0	0	0	35	0	0	0	0	0	0	0	0	0	0	0	0	0	0
e3	0	22	0	0	0	0	0	25	0	0	0	0	0	0	0	0	0	0	0	0	0
d3	0	0	0	0	0	0	0	0	0	0	0	0	0	0	0	0	0	0	0	0	0
e3	0	0	0	0	0	0	0	0	0	0	0	0	0	0	0	0	0	0	0	0	0
f3	0	0	0	0	0	0	0	0	0	0	0	0	0	0	0	0	0	0	0	0	0
g3	0	0	0	0	0	0	0	0	0	0	0	0	0	0	0	0	0	0	0	0	0
h3	0	0	0	22	0	0	0	0	0	0	0	0	0	0	0	0	0	0	0	0	0
c4	0	0	0	0	0	0	0	0	0	0	0	0	0	0	0	0	0	0	0	0	0
h4	0	0	0	0	0	0	0	0	0	0	0	0	0	0	0	0	0	0	0	0	0

Figure 5. The state space for the Lasker study after processing to select configurations in which White has a unique winning move

From a3 White can go to b3, b2 and a2 whose table entries are respectively
10, 05, and 60 indicating that Black, who is now to move, has after these
three White moves a draw, a loss in 5 and a draw. Clearly 1 Kb2 is White's
best, and for all Black replies the process can be continued until the complete solution has been derived.

ARE THERE ANY MORE STUDIES?

Solving a given position is not the only use to which the array can be
put. A table such as figure 4 provides a complete summary of the situation
for a given pawn configuration and can be used in a number of ways to
search for king position pairs with certain properties. In particular we can

Figure 6. The coding for the White king moves

hope to generate some more 'studies' by looking for positions where White
has only one move to win, hopefully a surprising one. Figure 5 shows the
result of processing figure 4 in such a way as to select positions with this
property. Non-zero entries indicate that for the corresponding king position
pair White to move has only one way to win, the first digit shows the depth
and the second the winning move coded as in figure 6. The Lasker study is
clearly shown, so too is a modification of it suggested by Reichhelm where
the WK is on a1 and the BK on a7. The table entry is 85, a win at depth 8
by Kb1, a subtle and surprising move after which the solution goes 1 Kb1
Kb7, 2 Kc1 Kc7, 3 Kd1 and now if Kc8, 4 Kd2 or Kd7 or Kd8, 4 Kc2 Kc8,
5 Kd2, etc. A look through the table in figure 5 suggests that these two
studies exhaust the artistic possibilities of this particular pawn configuration.

SITUATIONS IN WHICH THERE IS A PAWN RACE

For simplicity we have considered these positions from the point of
view of the white king trying to reach one of the critical squares with Black
defending on ranks 6, 7 and 8 only, and the results given above are valid
only for those cases in which Black can at no stage afford to counter-attack
White's f-pawn via h5 and g4 while its owner is otherwise engaged on the
queen's side. For example WK on g3, BK on h6 we took as a win for White
with him to move, whereas in fact since $B_r < W_1$ White is reduced to defence.
Since this talk was given A.Macdivitt of the Paisley College of Technology
has sent me a more detailed analysis of these situations and with his per-
mission I reproduce the gist of his work here.

If the criterion for a depth 1 White win is taken as $W_r < B_r$ or $W_1 < B_1$
and $W_1 \leqslant B_r$ with the additional proviso that White *cannot* win if $B_r \leqslant W_r$
and $B_r < W_1$, W to move, and $B_r \leqslant W_r$ and $B_r \leqslant W_1$, B to move, then there
is just one position given above as a White win which is now not, namely
WK on g3, BK on h8. More restrictively, if the criterion is taken as $W_r < B_r$
or ($W_1 < B_1$ and $W_1 < B_r$), then the Lasker study still stands but the Reichhelm study does not because the latter depends on the positions WK on c2
($W_1 = 2, W_r = 5$), BK on e7 or e8 ($B_1 = 3, B_r = 2$) in which $W_1 < B_1$ but
$W_1 = B_r$ being regarded as wins for White. These positions can be reached
if Black instead of 4 ... Kc8 plays Ke7 or e8 when White in order to win

must subject himself to a queening race in which he is only narrowly the victor. Such analysis is naturally beyond the scope of the simple method outlined above, which one could say found the Lasker study for the right reason, but the Reichhelm study for the wrong one.

Apart from the tactical uncertainties of simultaneous queening, which are always going to cause difficulty in this type of ending, can any conclusions be drawn about the usefulness of this approach in other king and pawn endings? Situations in which the pawns are not blocked can be completely changed by a single pawn move because the king distances may no longer be valid. Furthermore, the reserve tempi that available pawn moves provide must be allowed for. But since the method described above is not just feasible but computationally trivial it can be used as a terminal node evaluator for a more global analysis in which pawn moves are the significant transformations. As such this should be viewed as a small but useful tool in the construction of more general programs.

REFERENCE

Averbakh, Y. & M. Maizelis (1974) *Pawn Endings*. Batsford.

An Analysis of Minimax

D. F. Beal

INTRODUCTION

Minimax search using a heuristic evaluation function is known to be an effective technique for game playing. However, despite its widespread use, there is, as far as the present writer can discover, no published mathematical analysis showing why values backed up from minimax search are more trustworthy than the heuristic values themselves.

This paper presents an analysis of a very simple minimax model which yields the unsatisfactory conclusion that fixed-depth backed-up values are slightly *less* trustworthy than heuristic values themselves. Some possible reasons are offered but further work is necessary before the problem is fully understood.

Also described is a general algorithm based on simple assumptions about the probabilities of error in terminal and backed-up values which searches without depth or width limits until it achieves a backed-up value of suitable reliability. Two well-known and apparently different specific algorithms used successfully in practical chess-playing programs correspond to this general algorithm.

A SIMPLIFIED MINIMAX MODEL

This model is constructed to be simple enough to analyse so that the following question can be answered for it: 'By how much are backed-up values from a fixed-depth, exhaustive, minimax search more reliable than the heuristic values themselves?'

Assumptions

1. Tree structure with uniform branching factor b
2. Node values are either: win for player A
   or: win for player B
3. True values have the minimax relationship
4. Values are distributed so that at each level, the proportion of wins for the player to move is the same. (This enables the effect of n-ply search to be deduced directly from the effect of 1-ply search.)
5. Heuristic values are usually identical to true values, the proportion of erroneous values being small compared to $1/b$.
6. Heuristic values have a probability of error p, independent of the distribution of true values.

N.B. Values are denoted here by + and −, *but* + denotes a win for the player to move, rather than for either player A or player B. − denotes a loss for the player to move.

We achieve (4) by: Let terminal nodes have a probability k of being unfavourable for the player to move. That is, the proportion of $-$ nodes is k, the proportion of + nodes is $1 - k$. This will be the same probability for all nodes in the tree if k is the solution of:

$$(1 - x)^b = x$$

In other words, this condition ensures that the proportion of wins for either player is the same at depth $d + 2$ as at depth d, and the inverse of the proportion at depth $d + 1$.

Analysis

What are the probabilities of error in 1-ply backed-up values? We split the possible occurrences of true values into three cases:

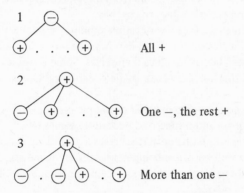

1   All +

2   One $-$, the rest +

3   More than one $-$

Probability of occurrence	Probability of error in backed-up value
1. $(1 - k)^b = k$	$1 - (1 - p)^b$
2. $b.k.(1 - k)^{b-1} = b.k.k/(1 - k)$	approximately p, since the assumption of low error rates means that more than one descendent node in error is second order
3. $1 - k - b.k.k/(1 - k)$	0, by assumption of low error rates

Case 1 gives rise to the only $-$ nodes at the 1-ply level. Case 2 gives rise to the only + nodes at the 1-ply level that have significant probability of error.

Let p' denote the probability of error in 1-ply backed-up values. Therefore:

$$p' = k.[1 - (1 - p)^b] + b.k.k/(1 - k).p$$

Again using the assumption of a low error rate, an approximation to $1 - (1 - p)^b$ is $b.p$. Hence

$$p' \approx k.b.p + b.k.k/(1 - k).p$$
$$= k.b.[1 + k/(1 - k)].p$$

Some numerical values for $k.b.[1 + k/(1 - k)]$ are:

$b = 2$ 1.24
$b = 5$ 1.62
$b = 10$ 1.97
$b = 20$ 2.37
$b = 40$ 2.82

A crude approximation may be made by taking $k = 1/(b + 1)$, which yields $k.b. [1 + k/(1 - k)] = 1$. In other words, no change in the probability of error.

A better approximation for large b may be made using the fact that k asymptotically approaches $(\log b)/b$ for large b. Hence p' approaches $(\log b).p$.

Result

In other words, for large branching factors, the probability of error is *increased* by the logarithm of the branching factor for every ply of search.

Conclusion

This result is disappointing. It was hoped that the analysis would show that the probability of error reduced with backing-up. Clearly this model does not capture the essential properties of minimax in typical game trees. It is not so clear, however, why this is so.

The analysis is of fixed-depth search and there are both empirical and intuitive grounds for believing that a suitable selective search will be far more effective than a similar-size fixed-depth search. Nevertheless, even fixed-depth search is well-known to yield substantial benefits in practice and so the fixed depth cannot be singled out as a satisfactory reason for the negative result.

Discounting the possibility of a mistake in the analysis, the following might be thought possible explanations:

1. Errors in heuristic values may not be distributed independently of the true values: they may be related in such a way as to render minimax search more useful.

2. The notion of probability of error as a measure of the usefulness of minimax values may be inappropriate. (Game-playing requires the choice of a move, not a judgement about the absolute value of positions.)

3. The distribution of true values in typical game trees may differ from the model in such a way as to render minimax search more useful.

4. The restriction to two values may be too extreme. Perhaps a range of values is needed so that errors in the heuristic value might be graduated, with large errors being less likely than small errors.

5. It may be necessary to assume different ranges of values for heuristic values and true values. E.g: True values of $+1$ and -1 but heuristic values drawn from the real numbers in between.

6. The assumption of very low probabilities of error may be inappropriate.

The problem is tantalizing: minimax search is so well-known to be useful that one expects a simple convincing explanation of why.

CONSISTENCY SEARCH

Fixed-depth, exhaustive search, whether it can be analysed or not, can be assumed to decrease the probability of error.

What I have termed consistency search is a method of decreasing the probability of error by selective searching. It is based on the following four assumptions:

1. Tree structure with true values having a minimax relationship.

2. Each node has a heuristic value which = true value + error value.

3. Low error rates.

4. All error values have a probability p of being non-zero, independently of values at any other nodes.

A node is consistent if its heuristic value is the same as the backed-up value from a 1-ply search over its descendants.

Assumption (4) implies that a 1-ply backed-up value and the heuristic value applied directly are independent estimates of the node's value. Taking the apparently conservative assumption that 1-ply backed-up values have the same probability of error as heuristic values themselves (ignoring the disturbing conclusion of the previous analysis), the probability of error if they agree is $p.p$. Hence consistent values are much more reliable than direct heuristic values.

A consistency search returns a value derived from consistent values. Its simplest implementation is a depth-first search terminating only at consistent nodes, as illustrated by the following pseudo-program:

HV = heuristic value for the current node
    (assumed to use the 'negamax' convention under which numeri-greater values are better for the current side to move, rather than for a fixed side.)

CV1 (consistency search value) =
begin v := −infinity
    foreach branch b *do*
        traverse(b); v := max(v, −HV); retrace(b)
    if (v = HV) return(v)
    v := −infinity
    foreach branch b *do*
        traverse(b); v := max(v, −CV1); retrace(b)
    return(v)
end

A version taking advantage of alpha-beta cutoffs:

HV2(a, β) = heuristic value bounded by a and β
CV2(a, β) =
begin v := a
    foreach branch b *do*
        traverse(b); v := −HV2$(−\beta, −v)$; retrace(b)
    if (HV2(a, β) = v) return(v)

```
          v := a
          foreach branch b do
              traverse(b); v := −CV2(−β, −v); retrace(b)
              if (v = β) return(v)
          return(v)
    end
```

Consistency Cutoffs

In addition to alpha-beta cutoffs it is possible to exploit 'consistency' cutoffs. These can occur at inconsistent nodes after one or more descendants have been searched. If the reliable value(s) thereby found render the node consistent when used in place of the direct heuristic values for those descendants, there is no need to search the remaining descendants. For example:

Heuristic values: 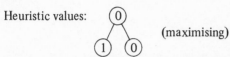   (maximising)

is inconsistent. Suppose that, after searching below the lefthand descendant, a consistent value of 0 is obtained for it. This consistent value is much more reliable than the direct value of 1. If it overrides the direct value, the inconsistency of the original node disappears. The righthand node can be cut off.

These consistency cutoffs do not reduce the expected reliability of the result (although, unlike alpha-beta, they may change it).

To incorporate consistency cutoffs into the search requires storing the heuristic values of all the descendant nodes if repeated evaluations are to be avoided. The stored values can be used to order the branches which has the important effect of ensuring that only the errant node is searched at nodes which are inconsistent because of a single high-valued descendant (the majority).

The following pseudo-program illustrates a consistency search taking advantage of consistency cutoffs.

```
    CV3 (consistency search using consistency cutoffs) =
    begin array B
          function maxB = largest value in B
          foreach branch b do
              traverse(b); B [b] := −HV; retrace(b)
          hv = HV
          if (maxB = hv) return(hv)
          sort B and the branches into descending order
          v := −infinity
          foreach branch b do
              traverse(b); B[b] := −CV3; v := max(v, B[b] ); retrace(b)
              if (maxB = hv) return(hv)
          return(v)
    end
```

A version with alpha-beta as well:

$CV4(a, \beta) =$
begin array B
  function maxB = largest value in B
  foreach branch b *do*
   traverse(b); B[b] := $-HV2(-\beta, -a)$; retrace(b)
  hv = $HV2(a, \beta)$
  if (maxB = hv) return(hv)
  sort B and the branches into descending order
  v := a
  foreach branch b *do*
   traverse(b); B[b] := $-CV4(-\beta, -v)$; v := max(v, B[b]); retrace(b)
   if (v = β) return(v)
   if (maxB = hv) return(hv)
  return(v)
 end

All these versions of consistency search are intended to make clear the basic algorithm and not to be immutable. In particular, in the case of chess capture search below, obtaining the values of the heuristic function down each branch by traversing the branch, applying the heuristic function, and retracing the branch is unnecessary when the heuristic function is material balance in chess: the change in material balance is readily obtainable as a by-product of generating the moves.

Practical Algorithms
Capture Tree Analysis in Chess. The usual way to perform a complete capture tree analysis, as implemented in several chess programs, uses the following rules:
(a) All captures are searched.
(b) A position where the side to play has no captures is terminal, and the static material balance value is taken.
(c) At any node, if all the captures for the side to play prove un-successful, the static material balance value is taken.
Of course, the second two of the four assumptions earlier, used to lend plausibility to the definition of consistency search, might not be true of capture analysis in chess.
Nevertheless, capture analysis corresponds exactly to consistency search using material balance as the heuristic value. Rules (b) and (c) correspond exactly to consistency and consistency cutoff.
Forward Pruning. The basic principle of forward pruning is to cut off descendant nodes with a static evaluation lower than the current best backed-up value.
The static evaluation is typically complex and there are many variants of the pruning rule. Optimistic and pessimistic versions bias the comparison to encourage or discourage cut-offs. Often the bias varies with depth. The authors of one chess program call their version razoring.

Nevertheless, the basic principle can be interpreted as the consistency cut-off rule within a consistency search.

However, to do so, the pruning rule must obey one other constraint. Namely, that it should not be applied if the static value at the current node is greater than the current best backed-up value. (Because then the node is still inconsistent.)

This additional rule is not mentioned in the literature and it would be interesting to know whether it has been used.

ACKNOWLEDGMENT

I am indebted to Mike Clarke for generously helping in several discussions and correcting errors.

The Behaviour of
a Chess Combination Program using Plans

J.Pitrat

This paper presents succinctly the principles of the program, but its main purpose is to study the behaviour of the program when it finds different kinds of combinations. As a result of this study, it examines some ways to improve the program, and in conclusion looks for some other uses for plans in a chess playing program.

The goal of this paper is not to give a full description of the program; this can be found in Pitrat (1977). The purpose is to study the behaviour of the program and to deduce from this behaviour some ways of improving it. I will start by briefly enunciating the principles on which the program is based.

DESCRIPTION OF THE PROGRAM

The program aims to find a combination in a given position. It tries only to find combinations where it can win an opposing piece. A combination exists if the first player has a material advantage whatever his opponent moves subsequently.

First the program carefully analyses the given position. It looks particularly for the men that are not protected or that are attacked and protected by the same number of men, so that it would be possible to capture them if they were attacked by one more man. From this analysis, the program generates some initial plans, which fall into one of the following categories:

1. Creation of a double attack. Pinning a man is a special case of a double attack.

2. Attacking vulnerable men. For instance: discovered attack, attacking a pinned man, cancelling the protection of a man ...

3. Attacking low mobility men. I have implemented only the case of the pawn and of the king. For the king, the program only considers two kinds of check moves: (a) the checks such that, after the move, all the squares where the king might move are controlled, except eventually the square occupied by the attacking man; (b) the checks such that the attacking man cannot be captured.

4. Promoting pawns that are on the sixth or seventh rank.

To simplify the program, some types of plan have not been considered, although they are necessary in some cases. The main defects are the generation of moves for attacking pieces that have temporarily a low mobility, as well as the generation of moves to threaten mate, but do not give a check. My goal was to see if the method could give some results, not to realize immediately a part of a chess playing program.

The program generates plans which are sequences of actions. There are three main types of action.

1. The move. We have to consider this move and to add it to the tree. If the move is followed by an asterisk, we can execute the following step of the plan, even if the move is not legal.

2. The modification: $S E_1 \rightarrow E_2$. S designates a square. E_1 is the state of the square S before the modification and E_2 the state after the modification. A state is represented by V for empty, E for enemy (it may be followed by the first letter of a man if we want a specific man), F for friend. If the first letter is an N, we want a state which is not the state defined by the letters following N. For example:

d4 NEK → EK. The enemy king is not on d4 and we want him there.

e5 E → V. There is an enemy man on e5; we want this square empty. This is useful if the enemy man is an obstacle that we want to eliminate because it prevents, for instance, a move of one of our rooks.

3. The verification: S E. S designates a square and E a state. If the square S does not have the state E, we leave the plan. For example:

e5 V. We do not execute the following statement of the plan if the square e5 is not empty.

The program first tries to execute the initial plans. If it succeeds, the opponent tries to counter them; for this, it uses exactly the same methods it uses when it takes the place of the first player. So, I presume that we always consider the first player. If something goes wrong, the program analyses the reasons for the failure and detects the opponent's moves that, if no longer possible, would offer a combination to the player. It chooses one of them, let's call it Q, and tries to analyse the possibilities arising from this move. It may:

1. Act before the enemy move Q. The program adds a modification statement at the beginning of the plan that created the friendly move just before Q, so that after the realisation of this modification, the enemy move Q will not be legal or will not be good for the opponent. If the enemy queen was on f5 and played move Q, we can place at the beginning of the new plan:

f5 EQ → NEQ

This statement will be followed by the original plan. Then move Q will not be legal.

2. Act after the enemy move. Perhaps Q was not really wrong, and the player may have a combination after Q. In that case, it is not possible to perform a detailed analysis of the situation: it would be too lengthy. The program makes several trials, and uses the results of the analysis performed in the initial position. If the method is good, there are not many unforeseen characteristics when we are moving from the initial position to the others. The first thing is to look for new possibilities of capture, i.e. moves that were not legal when the player played the preceding move. Then, if it does not succeed, it examines if, by chance, the opponent has not realised a modification that was the first step of a plan generated in the initial position. Lastly, it makes an analysis similar to the one performed for the initial

position, but restricted to the men that have just moved; in this case, the program does not consider plans with more than one modification.

When the program has to execute a modification statement, it calls a subroutine that tries to realise this modification. There are as many sub-routines as there are types of modifications. For instance, if we have the following modification: f5 E → NE. We do not want an enemy man on f5. The corresponding subroutine attempts three main possibilities: threatening the enemy man; capturing it; capturing a man protected by the enemy man on f5. So the program may find it natural to sacrifice one of its pieces.

THE BEHAVIOUR OF THE PROGRAM

There are three main types of behaviour. Naturally it happens in some cases that the program exhibits one type of behaviour when it finds the main variation and another type when it studies an opponent's reply. We notice that in all cases it is possible for the program, like a human chess player, to make mistakes. It may believe that there is a combination al-though in reality this is not true, because it has not considered an oppo-nent's possible reply. It may also believe that there is no combination, when in fact one exists, because it has not found the right move.

1. Combination Found by Reasoning

From the initial position the program has a definite idea of the combi-nation, and tries to realise it. It may be necessary to elaborate the initial plan. It is possible that this plan does not give the main variation, because the opponent must lose some material to avoid checkmate. When we have the main variation, the program tries to destroy it; generally, it looks for another combination after the player's moves. Then it is necessary to ex-amine these counter-combinations, and a large tree is developed. Usually there are many enemy moves at each level; this is especially clear when the player wins only a small material advantage. The more difficult combi-nations are those where we can win only one pawn. If there are one or several sacrifices in the first moves, it is not very difficult to prove that the player wins if the opponent captures the sacrificed man. The problem be-gins when the sacrifice is not accepted and when the opponent counter-attacks. The positions are very intricate: the sacrificed man is *en prise*, and so are the men that are counterattacked. Chess books do not usually say anything about what happens in that case. When we have this kind of be-haviour it happens frequently that the move that is finally chosen at the first level of the tree was not considered by any of the initial plans. This move is generated only so as to destroy a potentially inconvenient move on the part of the opponent, and it would be stupid to consider it *a priori*.

An example is shown in figure 1, M38. The program finds the combi-nation after 4870 plans and 22.35 seconds.

1	h2-h3	Qg4×h3
2	Qf2×f3	Rf8×f3
3	Rc5-c8+	Bd7×c8
4	Re5-e8+	Rf3-f8
5	Re8×f8++	

Figure 1. M38: White to play

We have the main characteristics of this scheme. The basic idea is the plan:

    f8   E → V
    c5   c8
    c8   h8

A white rook on the eighth rank would in fact mate the black king if we first remove the black rook. To remove the black rook, we can threaten it, with the queen for instance. We get the new plan

    f2   f3
    f3   f8*
    f8   V
    c5   c8
    c8   h8

But if we play Qf2×f3, the opponent plays Qg4×f3 and the rook on f8 is no longer threatened; f8 stays occupied. First we have to destroy the enemy move, for instance we can eliminate the black queen. So, we have:

    g4   EQ → NEQ
    f2   f3
    f3   f8*
    f8   V
    c5   c8
    c8   h8

To eliminate the black queen, we can threaten her. One possibility is to use the pawn on h2. Now it becomes logical to consider the move h2-h3. This move was not generated by any of the six plans which were found by the initial analysis. We get:

    h2   h3
    h3   g4*
    g4   NEQ
    f2   f3
    f3   f8*
    f8   V
    c5   c8
    c8   h8

This plan is the 46th plan generated by the program after the initial analysis

Figure 2. T113: White to play

and 4870 plans were necessary in all. All the other plans will be generated to verify this combination. The main work is not to find the combination, but to justify it. The opponent will try to counter this plan, for instance by capturing the rook on c8 or by intercepting with another piece. Then White tries to show that the enemy move is not sufficient and finds a new combination, for instance with the rook e5. The tree is very large; after the first White move, the program considers 19 enemy moves. After the second White move given further back, it considers 18 moves. If the sacrifice is not accepted, there are also some difficulties, but not too many in this case, because the first sacrificed man is only a pawn. If Black moves the queen instead of capturing the pawn, White will play Qf2×f3, and after this move the program considers 15 possible Black moves.

We have said that the main difficulty is not to find what is illustrated in chess books, but rather the moves which they do not discuss. Let us take an example: T113 (figure 2). The basic idea is to use the existing pin on the knight d4. White attacks it and Black tries to remove it or to protect it. After 500 plans, the program has found all the moves in the book. Tarrasch said: 'Black has made a serious mistake by pinning his own knight after playing Nc6×d4'. So White must win at least two pawns, since Tarrasch thinks that it is possible to gain some advantage although White has just lost one pawn. The program finds:

1	Qf3-f4	Nd4-e6
2	Qf4-a4+	Qb6-c6
3	Bd3-b5	any move
4	Bb5×c6	

It has also seen that after 1 ... e7-e5 2 Qf4×e5+, White also captures the knight. This covers all the moves discussed in the book. The program considers 20 Black moves after 1 Qf3-f4. For all of them, except 1 ... Nf6-e4, it shows that White wins at least two pawns. But it stopped after working a long time on what happens if Black replies Nf6-e4; it cannot find the right moves. In that case, there is probably a combination, but it is not easy to justify, because the position is very intricate. There is the Black threat Nd4-e2, so White cannot move his bishop d3. It is easy to show that White recaptures one pawn, but not so easy to show that he wins two pawns. We

Figure 3. M146: White to play

see that in the book we do not have the moves which are really difficult for the program. This position gave rise to the program's third failure (Pitrat 1977).

2. Combination found with a Sequence of Constraining Moves

In this case, the program has not, at the beginning, a precise idea of the combination that it will find. But it finds some moves that, if played, will give the opponent few possible replies. So it considers them, and after the opponent's replies it analyses the new position, but only for the men that have moved. It may find a plan, and in that case we have a combination that is a mixture of the first two types. But more generally there are new constraining moves and we resume the procedure. With a sequence of such moves, the program may find a combination that was unpredictable in the initial position. For example, M146 (figure 3): after 7262 plans and 26.11 seconds, the program finds the combination. The main variation is:

1	Qc4×f7+	Ng5×f7
2	e5-e6+	Qf5×e6
3	Nb7-c5+	Kd7-d8
4	Nc5×e6+	Kd8-d7
5	Ne6-c5+	Kd7-d8
6	Nc5-b7+	Kd8-d7
7	Bg2-h3+	f6-f5
8	Bh3×f5++	

At the beginning, the program has no precise idea. But it finds that if it plays Qc4×f7 Black can only play Ng5×f7. Move Qc4×f7 is considered because on f7 the queen controls all the squares where the enemy king can move. After Ng5×f7, it looks for a new way of attacking the black king. So, step by step, the program finds the combination.

Generally, such combinations began with plans based on a checking move. If it is the second type of check (check given by a man which cannot be captured), we generally have such a combination. But not always with the first type (the man gives a check and controls all the squares where the king can move, except the square where the man is). There are two possibilities:

Figure 4. M4: White to play

(a) it is good to sacrifice. The program looks for a combination after the sacrifice. Then we have behaviour of the second type.

(b) it is not good to sacrifice. We make a plan for controlling the square before playing this move. We then have behaviour of the first type. For instance M58, given in Pitrat (1977).

When it is not possible to play the check because some obstacle must be removed, we try to remove it; then we may have a combination of the first type (for instance M38 given above) or a combination of the second type. In that case, the plans are very useful, although we are using constraining moves.

It may happen that we have this type of behaviour, although the plan does not begin with the idea of attacking the king. The second type of combination occurs when some move modifies the board in such a way that it is not possible to foresee what happens later without reanalysing part of the position. This is the case after a move by the king, but also after the promotion of a pawn. The relations between the men are completely different after the promotion, and it is necessary to reanalyse the situation to try to find a new plan. This plan would be difficult to find before the promotion. For example, M4 (figure 4). In the initial position, the program looks for a plan promoting the pawn c7. It does not try to win a material advantage. It thinks that it might be interesting to consider the position after the promotion, even if it does not win a piece. The idea is to remove the queen, then to move the pawn. So, we get:

| 1 | Qb3-b5 | Qc6×b5 |
| 2 | c7-c8Q+ | Ke8-f7 |

This is not an acceptable result, since White loses a pawn, but these moves constrain Black, and the program analyses the new situation. It finds the idea of a double attack:

e6	NEK → EK
d5	c7
c7	e6*
c7	b5

The king is not on e6. To induce him to go somewhere, we can put him in check, by placing a man on this square. So we have:

Figure 5. M118: White to play

3	Qc8×e6+	Kf7×e6
4	Nd5-c7+	any move
5	Nc7×b5	

This double attack was not foreseen by the program in the initial position.

In such combinations, there is a succession of smaller combinations without any tie between them. When the combination has been found, it is easy to understand why it succeeded; but it is difficult to find in the initial position. It will probably always be necessary to consider such moves. For these combinations the main problem is not the number of enemy moves, since we choose those moves which limit his possible replies. The difficulty comes from the number of moves which may constrain the opponent. The problem is evident when there are several possible combinations. The program is searching simultaneously for all of them, and it stops only when it has found one of them. In that case, it wastes its time searching for the others, but it is difficult to avoid, because all these moves are important. For example, M118 (figure 5): the program finds the combination given by Stamma:

1	Qc5-e7+	Ke8×e7
2	Ne5-g6++	Ke7-d8
3	Ng5-f7+	Kd8-c8
4	Ng6-e7++	

But by this time it has almost found a second combination. It has already found:

1	Ne5×d7+	Nf6-e4
2	Re2×e4+	Ke8-d8
3	Qc5×c7+	Kd8×c7
4	Ng5-e6+	Kc7-c8
5	Nd7×b6++	

and it has seen that if 1 ... Qh5×e2, then 2 Nd7×f6++. It has still to analyse what happens after 1 ... Ke8-d8. It can certainly do this, since it is almost the same variation it has already found: in the first case, there is only one more move: an interception by the knight on e4. In both cases, the program has no precise view of the final step, it only tries to pin the king down.

To solve the problem of the number of moves of the first player that can be considered in certain cases the program orders them, and then tries those that limit the opponent's replies. This method is similar to that given in Pitrat (1971). It is important, however, when we generate an opponent's move to examine it quickly to see if it is possible to make a simple and effective reply. Generally if a move does not lead to a combination the opponent will soon have many possible moves. This is the case when there is a sacrifice. If it is not a good idea as it entails losing a piece it is more difficult for the program to constrain as the enemy king has more possibilities of escape. So the program soon stops further analysis in this direction. But it happens sometimes that it is possible to give a large number of successive checks, and that after each of them the opponent has only one or two replies. When there is no capture of one's own men, the sequence of such moves may be lengthy. Unfortunately, the program does not have the possibility of seeing quickly that it has no hope of winning; a human player sees this more easily, and an improvement to the program would be to give it this capacity. This would eliminate the main reason for wasting time in such combinations.

3. Overlapping of Two Combinations

There are two cases. The first one is when the program foresaw the possibility of both combinations. We generate a plan where some modifications are needed. We do not find a way of realising these modifications, but it happens that further down in the tree, after moves where we try to realise another plan, the modifications are fulfilled. The opponent has realised them by avoiding another danger. Then we try to execute at this level the combination that was generated in the initial position. An example of this happens with M75 (Pitrat 1977). The first plan was a discovered attack on a rook after removing an enemy knight. The second plan was to create a double attack with a pawn. One way for the opponent to parry the fork was to capture the pawn with the knight. In that case, the program executed the first plan. This does not happen frequently for the first player. Generally this possibility is used by the opponent. He considers plans which he could make use of, if it was his move, and continues to envisage their use after the combination. One example was given with T149 (Pitrat 1977). This is a useful method for trying to win a man of the same value as that which was lost. The opponent uses the modifications that we have made on the board for the success of the combination. But there is no overlapping of combinations of the same player when the opponent uses this possibility.

In the second case, the program finds a combination by chance. A move was generated as a step in a plan, but this plan failed. The program analyses quickly the position after the move, and it discovers a new combination. In that case, the method has failed: the program finds the combination, but without seeing it in initial position. For example, M193 (figure 6): the basic idea is to move the black queen to g2 where she can effect checkmate. But the rook on d2 captures the queen. One possibility for rectifying this is to move a man to some intermediate square, for

Figure 6. M193: Black to play

instance e2; it is necessary that the man creates a threat at the same time. So we have the plan:

e2	V → NV
c6	g2
g2	g1

For this modification, we can move the knight on f4 to e2, so it puts the king in check. Thus we have

f4	e2
e2	g1*
e2	NV
c6	g2
g2	g1

But the opponent will play, after 1 Nf4-e2+, RD2×e2. The square e2 is not empty, but 2 Qc6-g2+ is still wrong, because the rook can always capture the queen. So the plan fails. But after a check, the program always analyses if there is a new possibility of attacking the king. It then finds checkmate by means of a succession of plans to constrain the king:

1		Nf4-e2+
2	Rd2×e2	Rf8-f1+
3	Kg1×f1	Qc6-h1+
4	Kf1-f2	Ne5-g4++

Nf4-e2 is not generated as a constraining move, because it does not control the square h2 where the king is free to move.

It is difficult to know when the situation occurs. We must print all the plans if we want to be sure that the program has found the right combination for a reason which is wrong. But the same thing may happen with human chess players. They may find a combination by chance, without foreseeing it. They may also consider a move for the wrong reason, and then discover that this move is right for another reason. In De Groot (1965) there is a protocol by Dr Euwe for position A. There are four exchanges and he considers them systematically one after the other. When he is analysing the third one, he begins to say: 'This must be looked into', then, after developing moves further down the tree, he is surprised to find: 'But that's good for White'.

SOME POSSIBLE IMPROVEMENTS

The first point is that it seems impossible to foresee all the possible combinations from the given situation. We cannot always generate the plan that gives the combination, so it is necessary to generate plans that contain constraining moves and to examine what is possible after them. However it is possible to improve the generation of plans. The initial analysis could be made in a better way and the program could use some concepts that it does not actually use. For instance with M38 (figure 1) it does not see that the bishop on d7 has two missions: to control c8 as well as e8. The program does not look for men that have too many roles to execute at the same time. There is no theoretical impossibility, but it is necessary to program the detection of this eventuality and the generation of the corresponding plans. In this direction, there are many things to do and it would be interesting to improve this part of the program.

The main problem in the first behaviour is the number of enemy moves to be considered. For this, we can do nothing: it derives from the nature of the problem. It is necessary to find quickly the right answer to these moves and the program is efficient in doing this. The level at which a correction is made does not lead to a failure, but it would probably be necessary to improve on this.

For the second type of behaviour, it would be possible to improve the generation of plans involving constraining moves. This could be done in two directions. First, to generate other kinds of constraining moves. In M193 (figure 6) Nf4-e2 could be considered as such a move: the opponent has only two replies and there are still many possibilities for attacking him. So it would be necessary to give the program the ability to create such a plan in situations where there were other possibilities of attacking a king that had several possible moves.

Secondly the program could eliminate in some cases moves that are checks, although the man giving the check cannot be captured. It might happen that it is possible to give a lot of successive checks without the possibility of checkmate. To eliminate such checks it is necessary to evaluate the likelihood of checkmating the enemy king. The improvement could be made together with another one: the generation of moves threatening mate. The same characteristics would be considered in both cases. This elimination would be very useful, because in some positions, the program wastes its time in giving checks when there is no hope of checkmate.

It is necessary to keep the possibility of finding combinations where several plans may interfere with each other. But with a new definition of constraining moves, we could certainly decrease the number of combinations found by chance. I know two cases of such combinations, and in both the right move could be generated correctly by the new definition. Perhaps one would be able to extend the possibility for interferences of plans to a small number of plans, which would be generated not only in the initial position but also at some node deeper in the tree. It would also be necessary to modify the analysis made after an enemy move that is wrong. It would certainly be better to make this analysis a little more detailed, as well as choosing more carefully the nodes where the program performs it.

It is certainly interesting to use such a program as part of a game-playing program. But a modification must be made to the program if we want to do this. Generally there is no combination or it is impossible to prove that there is a combination because there are too many replies for the opponent. It is, however, useful to find moves that would give the program the possibility of winning something after most of the replies open to the opponent, or at least not losing anything. After such moves, it is likely that the opponent does not find the right reply. It is easier to find this rather than to prove that we win something for all replies. The tree is very much smaller. For instance for M146 (figure 3) it is easy to prove that after the fourth move Nc5✕e6 the balance of the captures is zero; and in this position, there are always good possibilities for attacking. This would be a sufficient reason for playing the move. Certainly in some cases, human players stop the development of the tree as this level.

Other improvements may be considered. Some of them do not require a fundamental change of the program, it would only be necessary to change the analysis to create other types of plan, and the evaluation function. For instance the program could find combinations which give a positional advantage, those where one player tries to make exchanges if he has more material or where he attempts to bring about stalemate. Other changes would be more difficult to realise: for them, it would be necessary to define a new language for stating plans. One such application would be the use of strategic plans, as well as plans useful for the endgame with pawns. The idea of a plan is certainly useful, but it must have different elements. There may be modifications that require a large number of moves (for instance moving the king to a central square) or the description of some wanted state (for instance, our king must be in opposition to the opponent's one). It would be necessary to write a completely different program, but I believe that the basic methodology of this program would always be useful.

REFERENCES

De Groot, A.D. (1965) *Thought and Choice in Chess*. The Hague: Mouton.
Pitrat, J. (1971) A general game playing program, in *Artificial Intelligence and Heuristic Programming* (eds N.V.Findler & B.Meltzer) pp. 125-55. Edinburgh: University Press.
——— (1977) A chess combination program which uses plans. *Artificial Intelligence 8*, 275-321.

Mate at a Glance

J.A.Birmingham and P.Kent

ABSTRACT
Current tournament level chess programs use several different systems to detect checkmate within the game tree.

This paper discusses two popular systems and then describes a routine incorporated into the MASTER program which detects mate and certain forced mate situations ('pseudo' mate) at the static level.

A set of rules is given, by which mate or 'pseudo' mate positions may be recognised given a small amount of knowledge.

IINTRODUCTION

A chess player's 'one shot' look at the board is, in fact, rarely as simple an exercise as the recognition of a pattern. For many mate positions, the player has already played a sequence of moves (tree searched) which have forced the winning move. However, when suddenly confronted by a position in which there is a one-move mate, or a forced mate in n, even the expert player can miss the obvious and/or spend a considerable time 'tree searching' the board. If this were not true, the chess problemist would have a lean time! There are many (famous) examples in the chess literature of missed mates of this sort.

The modern chess program is rarely now diverted by such distractions as a queen *en prise* when there is a checkmate in the offing – provided, always, that the checkmate is: (a) within its lookahead; and (b) if within its lookahead, the program is capable of recognising the fact. There are several methods used to detect checkmate in game-trees, which may be summarised as shown in figure 1.

Both methods 1a and 1b need at least one extra ply from a mating move to verify that the position is in fact mate, and in game situations where time is short and a limited depth of search has to be employed (5 ply). Programs that use this method often cannot recognise mate in 2. As will be shown, method 1c can recognise a mate move at ply 1, a mate in 5 from ply 1, and has found mate in 9 using a 7-ply tree (18-ply mate!). The current MASTER program (level 4.6) uses a combination of methods 1b and 1c. Method 1b is used where method 1c would either prove too expensive or would involve third and fourth order effects.

KNOWLEDGE REQUIREMENTS FOR
STATIC MATE/PSEUDO MATE DETECTION

To implement 'mate at a glance' routines in a chess program, certain elements of information are essential, and some assumptions must be made

(a)

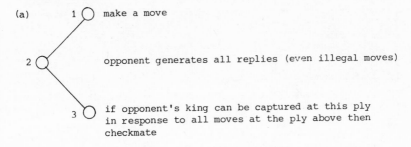

```
1 ◯  make a move

2 ◯       opponent generates all replies (even illegal moves)

  3 ◯    if opponent's king can be captured at this ply
         in response to all moves at the ply above then
         checkmate
```

(b)

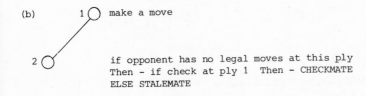

```
1 ◯  make a move

2 ◯       if opponent has no legal moves at this ply
          Then - if check at ply 1   Then - CHECKMATE
          ELSE STALEMATE
```

(c)

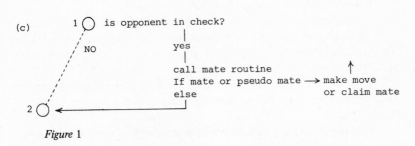

```
1 ◯  is opponent in check?
            |
    NO     yes
            |
          call mate routine
          If mate or pseudo mate ──→ make move
          else                       or claim mate
2 ◯ ◄──────────────────┘
```

Figure 1

with respect to the attacking/defensive powers of certain pieces, some obvious and some more subtle. They may be summarised as follows: (a) an explicit knowledge of the control which each piece has over any given square of the board; (b) a knowledge, for any given square, of the attacking piece, and its colour; and (c) 'X-ray' attacks, 'absolute' pins and implied pins.

In the MASTER program, a set of arrays is maintained by the Evaluation routine(s), which store the following information:

MC   The number of controls which 'my' pieces have on any given Board square.

YC   The number of controls which 'your' pieces have on any given Board square.

MP   The home squares of each of my pieces which control any given square.

YP   The home squares of each of your pieces which control any given square.

MX   Blocked vector information for my B,R,Q (X-rays)

YX   Blocked vector information for your B,R,Q (X-rays)

MBIAS   my King controls a list of squares adjacent to the Kings

YBIAS   your King controls a list of squares adjacent to the Kings

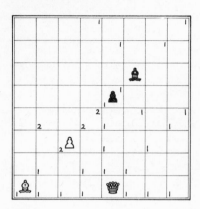

Figure 2   Figure 3

From the above, the program can – by simple table lookup – detect:

    a) which pieces attack/defend any given square

    b) which pieces are pinned by what and to what

    c) the degree of control, for either side, of squares around the kings

    d) which pieces prevent my or your pieces from attacking or defending significant squares of the board. E.g. if 'I' move 'your' piece, I could mate in a given square.

In order to make the above tables more useful, certain deductions have to be made about the attacking powers of certain pieces in special configurations.

(a) *Pawns*: can only attack/defend diagonally but block in a forward direction.

(b) *Bishops and Queens*: control extra squares when looking through pawns of their own colour, in the correct direction of travel.

From figure 2 it can be seen that the pawn on c3 puts 1 control on each of b4 and d4. The bishop on a1 controls squares b2, c3 and d4. Because in a swap-off sequence on d4, both pawn and bishop can take part; both b4 and d4 are doubly controlled by white, although this is not immediately obvious.

(c) *Vector Pieces (R,B,Q)*: When doubled (or tripled) in RR, RQ, BQ combinations add extra controls to 'X-rayed' squares.

From figure 3, we can see that the queen on a1 adds controls on the 'a' file to the squares controlled by the rook, and to the a1-h8 diagonal squares controlled by the bishop. N.B. that the square f6 is triply controlled by White due to the pawn case.

The *important exception* to the above cases is that the square containing the opponent's king *cannot* be controlled in this way. In figure 4 the square of the black king (a7) has only one control on it (that of the rook). If the extra control of the queen were considered effective then the position would be flagged as a 'double check', which is obviously incorrect. Note however, that the square behind the king (a8) is controlled by both rook and queen.

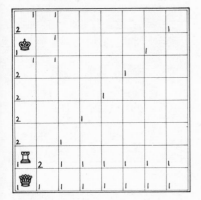

Figure 4

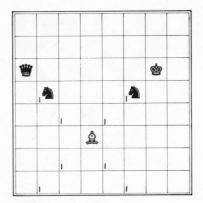

Figure 5

(d) *Implied controls (X-rays) by Vector Pieces (Pins)*: In figure 5, White's bishop on d3 has an 'X-ray' attack on the black queen on a6 and on the black king on g6. Thus both of Black's knights are pinned.

For 'mate at a glance' purposes, the two types of pin must be treated differently, since the pin on the knight on b5 is not absolute in that it can legally move; but the pin on the knight on f5 *is* absolute, since to move it would place the king in check.

(e) An often overlooked point: pieces do not control their home squares.

DETECTION OF MATES AND 'PSEUDO' MATES

From the above information, the following set of rules can be derived. (It should be noted at this point that we will give only the rules that have been implemented in MASTER, but will show the extensions of these rules that will be implemented in the future, and the reasons for their exclusion at this stage.) The rules may be used to detect: (a) checkmate, and (b) 'pseudo' mate, a position in which the opponent can only postpone mate by a series of useless blocks.

Given   the enemy king is in check (one of *my* pieces has a control on the square of the enemy king)
then   if all squares adjacent to the king are blocked by his pieces
or   controlled by my pieces
or   blocked by both my and his pieces and my pieces are defended (controlled by others of my pieces)
then   mate can be detected for the following cases:

1. For a checking piece, adjacent to the king, attacked only by the king (figure 6).
2. For a double check (figure 7).
3. For a knight which is not attacked (figure 8).
[*Note*. The logical extension of this case, e.g. a knight which is attacked

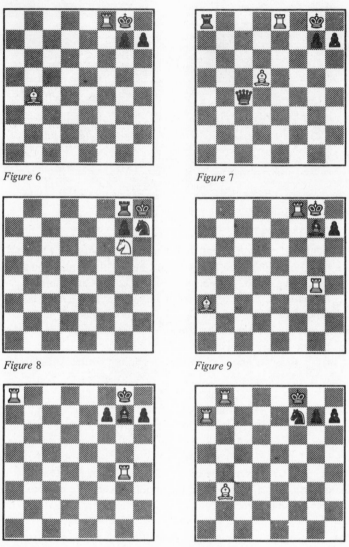

Figure 6

Figure 7

Figure 8

Figure 9

Figure 10

Figure 11

by one of your pieces but which is defended by my other knight, has not been implemented, because the following complications prove too expensive at present to compute, in that they require a high degree of recursion. E.g. the piece which attacks the first knight may, on capturing, reveal a secondary check on my king, or a pin on my second knight against my king, etc.]

4. For pieces adjacent to the king which are attacked only by pinned pieces – and the king (figure 9).

5. For vector pieces (rook, queen, bishop) on the rank, file or diagonal, subject to the following tests:

5a. Pieces which threaten to block on the square adjacent to the king must be pinned to the king (figure 10). The bishop on g7, if not pinned,

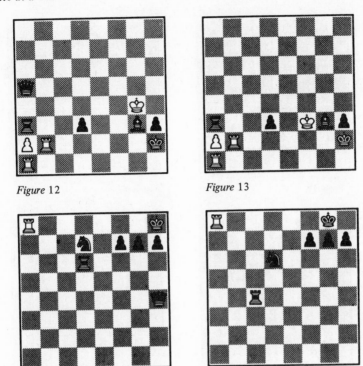

Figure 12

Figure 13

Figure 14

Figure 15

would successfully block on f8.

5b. Pieces which threaten to block do not create an escape square which 'I' do not control (figure 11). This is an example of a 'pseudo' mate. The block by the knight is useless since it is on a square which is not controlled by one of its own pieces and consequently can be taken.

5c. That you cannot block with a pawn on a square which is controlled by another of your pieces (figure 12: see also 5d). The pawn on d3 can successfully block the check since the square d2 is controlled by the queen. Note: blocks by the Q on d2 or the bishop on f2 would both be unsuccessful, e.g. pseudo mates would be claimed.

5d. That your blocking piece does not discover check on my king (figure 13). Although moving to an unprotected square, the pawn reveals a check on my king. The bishop block on f2 gives 'pseudo' mate.

5e. That blocking pieces do not reveal secondary blocks (figure 14). The knight block on b8 reveals a secondary block by the rook. (Nf8 or Qd8, Nf8 would both be pseudo mate.)

[Note: This is the current implementation. The logical extensions of this rule involve heavy recursive computing which is not economical.] e.g. 5.e.1. That blocking pieces do not reveal secondary blocks either adjacent to the king, or

5.e.2. on squares which are controlled by other pieces (figure 14).

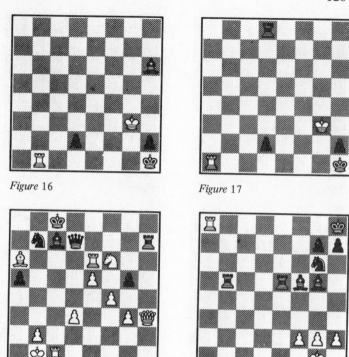

Figure 16

Figure 17

Figure 18

Figure 19

5.e.3. That blocking pieces do not reveal secondary blocks that in turn discover check on my king.

5.e.4. etc., etc.

5f. If you have *more than one control on a blocking square* and either piece is a knight or rook (figure 15; see also 5g).

5g. If you have more than one control on a blocking square, do bishop or queen control the square through a pawn? (figure 16). The position as shown is a 'pseudo' mate position. The pawn block is useless. However the square c1 is of interest since it is doubly controlled, by pawn and bishop. This case must be detected as an exception to the general rule that a doubly controlled square on the vector implies rule 5f.

5h. If you can block with a pawn, will the blocking square then be controlled by rook or queen? (figure 17). This is an exception to the rule that no squares on the vector are controlled by the opponent in that the apparently useless block by the pawn creates a control (by the rook).

then if you have no block moves on the checking vector *then checkmate*
else 'pseudo' mate. (Useless blocks defer mate.)

Note. For the current implementation of the routine, as soon as second, third, fourth, etc. order effects, other than those given above, are detected, then the program returns a flag instructing the tree searcher to follow the sequence. This technique is used to save time in what would otherwise be a very expensive routine.

SOME EXAMPLES

1. The position in figure 18, when tested, was claimed at ply 1 by the program after it had evaluated only two nodes (it looked at NxQ first), and .001 seconds of elapsed time. Prior to the inclusion of the routine, the program needed 2 ply (3 ply by the figure 1a example) to find the mate.

2. The position in figure 19 was equivalent to a mate in 11 ply for MASTER (mate in 12 or 13 ply for conventional methods). It was detected at ply 1 and was the first node examined. If detected at ply 7 of the tournament program, it would enable the program to claim 'mate in 17 ply', e.g. mate in 9, which is outside the range of most conventional programs (if not all).

SPIN OFF

1. Application to Tree Pruning

The main routine, which is now a permanent feature of the MASTER program, is called at all plies of the tree when a check is detected. Apart from its immediate value in detecting certain classes of mate and 'forced mates', it has proved surprisingly effective in pruning the game tree. Branches can be cut ruthlessly when a mate position is detected, generally 1-2 plies earlier than with conventional methods.

Figure 20

When coupled with the feedover technique, which ensures that profitable lines/moves are examined early in the tree, it can considerably reduce the number of nodes examined at each ply. Consider the position shown in figure 20. The following table shows the nodes/ply from a 5 ply run in which the position occurred. Figures are given for the program with (a) no mate routine; (b) mate routine giving mate scores but not cutting the tree; and (c) mate routine used to cut the tree.

Ply	(a)	(b)	(c)
1	42	42	42
2	1809	1303	530
3	525	231	184
4	2861	1761	793
5	1982	262	262
	7219	3599	1811

A gain of approximately 74% was made in the tree at a cost of approximately 2% in the evaluation routine.

2. Detection of 'Interesting' Squares

For example, in figure 21 the rook could deliver mate on square a8, if the bishop could be captured or moved.

Figure 21

The routine has been modified to 'flag' any move which attacks pieces which control a square in which mate would otherwise be possible. In the example, moves Na5, Nd6, (Ra7, Ra8) would all be flagged, and the tree search would then be instructed to examine in depth the effects of the swap-offs.

The overall effect of the modification (which is currently being re-searched) is that the program now shows a degree of planning in its play, which has had a marked effect in some aspects of its game.

REFERENCE

Kent, P. & J.A. Birmingham (1980) The MASTER Chess Program (this volume

The MASTER Chess Program

P. Kent and J. A. Birmingham

This paper is a description of the techniques implemented in our chess program MASTER.

TREE-SEARCHING
Procedure PICKBESTMOVES
This is called at all levels of the tree-searching process to select and order moves to be examined further. The number of moves selected at any level is not fixed. It will frequently select and order the complete list and at other times will discard the whole list. The process is as follows:

(a) All moves are listed.
(b) Each move is made in turn and the resulting position evaluated. The evaluation function eliminates all moves that leave the king in check.
(c) The FEEDOVER (see later) list is examined to see if a move has been placed there from previous evaluations of the decision tree. If so, this is ordered to the top of the list.
(d) The moves are ordered according to the static evaluation.
(e) The static scores are compared with previous backed up values. Some or all of the moves may be discarded.
(f) Some very tactical moves are now forced into the list, however low their static value.

Pruning the Tree
The moves are taken from the list, in order, for examination at the next ply. As each move is completed its backed-up value is compared with the static value of the next move to see if the rest of the list can be discarded. Various techniques for pruning the tree during the search and in the selection process, i.e. Razoring (Birmingham and Kent 1977) and Marginal Forward Prune (Birmingham and Kent 1977, Slagle 1971) to discard moves that should be searched when the static evaluation oscillates over a wide range as the search is deepened. To overcome this, we tried cutting the tree on the minimum of the backed-up score and the static score from various earlier plies. We also forced in the tactical moves, which tend to be the ones that cause wild fluctuations in the evaluation. This solved most of the problems, but at the cost of a much wider tree search. We are now experimenting with the methods suggested by Beal (1980); the first results look encouraging.

Feedover
Feedover is a technique for using previously computed information to

force good moves to the head of the list. It improves the effectiveness of all the tree-pruning techniques used in the program. The FEEDOVER list is examined at every ply to see if there is a move at that depth, and if so, whether it can be matched with one of the available moves. If so it is forced to the head of the list. There are two mechanisms for putting moves into the FEEDOVER list:

(a) The 'best' line in response to the opponent's chosen move is taken from information stored during the tree search for the previous move.

(b) Any move that improves the backed-up score at this depth. This is referred to as the Refutation Technique or the Killer Heuristic (Birmingham and Kent 1977, Bell 1973). Once the FEEDOVER mechanism is set up it is extremely easy to add the Refutation Technique.

To save the whole tree from one move for use on the next move would be very expensive, so we save only one line for each of the opponent's likely replies at ply 2. A table is produced giving a 'best' line for the twenty or so best moves available to the opponent. This table is printed out and provides very valuable information about the program's reasons for making a given move. After the opponent has made his move, the program scans the table for a match, it then loads the FEEDOVER list with the 'best' line as taken from the table. The FEEDOVER move at ply 1 is usually accepted in over 70% of the cases.

THE EVALUATION FUNCTION

Some chess programs use a very simple evaluation function, based almost entirely on material, and search the decision tree very thoroughly to a limited depth, perhaps following captures and checks to a greater depth. Others perform a very elaborate move selection and/or evaluation, searching only a very limited part of the decision tree. In practice the former seems to be more successful over a complete game as it is less likely to make the tactical blunders that lose a game instantly. We try to adopt a middle approach by analysing a position as well as possible while maintaining a minimum speed of about 500 position evaluations per second.

Most evaluation functions give a very heavy weighting to material values. MASTER is no exception, but unlike some programs the total weight given to positional features can easily exceed the value of a pawn. The greatest penalties are associated with threats to the king, which was found to be essential to avoid simple sacrificial mating attacks. For example, moving the king towards the centre of the board in the middle game would be penalised progressively up to the value of about one pawn. Control of squares next to the king by a queen in association with other pieces could collect a penalty of considerably more than a pawn. The penalty is dependent on the collective power of the pieces making the attack.

At present the evaluation function detects the following factors:

(a) Material value.

(b) Value of swapping off on the squares of each of the pieces.

(c) Attacks on defended pieces.

(d) Hidden attacks: pins, X-rays, skewers.

(e)   Checkmate, pseudo mate (Birmingham and Kent 1980), stalemate, repetition of position, check.

(f)   Position of pieces, e.g. knights are weak at the edges of the board, bishops are good in knight 2.

(g)   Pawns increase in value as they advance.

(h)   The king is encouraged to go to knight 1 at the start and to the middle in the end game.

(i)   Control of squares.

(j)   Threats to squares next to the king.

(k)   Rooks and queens on open or half-open files.

(l)   Doubling of rooks, queens and bishops.

(m)   Passed pawns: increase rapidly as they advance. Their value is increased in the end game.

(n)   Attacking passed pawns, the squares in front of passed pawns and blocking passed pawns, rooks behind passed pawns.

(o)   The 'square' of the passed pawn, i.e. it can not be caught by the opponent's king.

(p)   Relative position of opposing unstoppable passed pawns, i.e. which one queens first.

(q)   In king and pawn end games, kings do not threaten the backward of two passed pawns. If the king captures, then it cannot stop the other pawn queening.

(r)   Doubled pawns, backward pawns, isolated pawns, blocking backward pawns (holes).

(s)   Bishop/pawns colour complex.

(t)   Distance of kings from the pawn mass in king and pawn end games.

(u)   Moving kings together (essential for piece end games).

(v)   Opposition of kings.

(w)   Keeping king and pieces together, or apart (important in some piece end games).

(x)   Castling.

SYNTHESIS PHASE
Various arrays contain information about the position.

MYSQ, YRSQ
   These two arrays record the position of each of my pieces and your pieces on the board. MYSQ(0) and YRSQ(0) keep a count of the effective length of the two arrays. The pieces are always positioned in the same place in the array. The pawns are packed down as they are captured to shorten the length of the array that has to be scanned. In the initial position the array corresponding to white would contain:
   18 5 4 1 8 3 6 2 7 9 10 11 12 13 14 15 16 66 67
(squares are numbered from 1 for White's QR1 to 64 for Black's KR1.)
   Thus, there are 18 white men on the board. The king is in square 5, the queen in 4, the rooks in 1 and 8, the bishops in 3 and 6, etc. The two extra pieces in squares 66 and 67 are pseudo-pieces corresponding to king-

side and queen-side castling. As pieces are captured their position is set to square 65.

BOARD, MYMAN, YRMAN

BOARD records the type of piece on each square of the board, i.e. white pawn = 1, black pawn = 7, knight = 2, bishop = 3, rook = 4, queen = 5, king = 6, castling move (pseudo-piece) = 8 for queen side and 9 for king side. MYMAN and YRMAN are the same as BOARD but record only my pieces and your pieces respectively.

To make a move in the tree these five arrays are modified. The changes are recorded in other arrays so that the position can be reset as one backs up the tree, see Bell (1970).

MYCONTROLS, YRCONTROLS, MYPIECES, YRPIECES

The first positional feature we ever added to the program was attack on the centre squares. It was computed by counting up the number of threats each side had on each square of the board and comparing them. This rather crude measure of control has undergone various refinements since, but the principal of control of squares has been the basis of virtually all further work on the evaluation function.

As each new position is generated the program goes first through a synthesis phase during which information about the position is collected into a number of arrays, from which it can be extracted efficiently during the later analysis phase. The most important of these arrays are MYCON-TROLS, YRCONTROLS, MYPIECES and YRPIECES.

MYCONTROLS and YRCONTROLS give a count of the number of my pieces and your pieces attacking each of the 64 squares on the board. MYPIECES and YRPIECES are two-dimensional arrays giving a list of the squares of the pieces attacking each square of the board, i.e. MYPIECES(I, J) is the square of my Ith piece attacking square J. The lists in MYPIECES and YRPIECES are ordered so that the lowest-valued piece attacking a square is first. The order is modified, however, to take account of, for example, bishops attacking squares through queens, where of course, any swap-off sequence requires capture by the queen before action by the bishop.

Bishops and queens control one square diagonally through their own pawns in the direction that the pawn captures. Your king is always trans-parent to my vector pieces. However, two or more vector pieces attacking the king along one vector add only one control on the square containing the king. This is to avoid errors when looking for double check in the 'mate at a glance' routine (Birmingham and Kent 1980).

If MY corresponds to white then for square d4 in figure 1 the four arrays contain the following:

MYCONTROLS(28) = 4	number of my controls on square 28
YRCONTROLS(28) = 2	number of your controls on square 28
MYPIECES(1, 28) = 19	square containing the white pawn
MYPIECES(2, 28) = 4	square containing the white rook
MYPIECES(3, 28) = 10	square containing the white queen

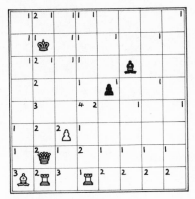

Figure 1   *Figure* 2

MYPIECES(4, 28) = 1   square containing the white bishop
YRPIECES(1, 28) = 37   square containing the black pawn
YRPIECES(2, 28) = 46   square containing the black bishop

Notice that the white bishop is last in the list, being after the two higher-valued pieces, the white rook in d1 and the white queen in b2. The bishop is looking through the queen at square d4 and can therefore only take action after the queen. The rook, being of lower value, takes precedence over the queen and hence over the bishop.

MXTH, YXTH

Whenever the path of a vector piece (queen, rook, bishop) is found to be blocked, information is stored in either MXTH or YXTH. The first element of each array records the number of elements used in the array. Four items are then stored for each blocked vector.

(a)   The first square beyond the X-rayed piece.
(b)   The end square of the vector.
(c)   The step length of the vector.
(d)   The square containing the vector piece.

If MY corresponds to White then for the position in figure 2 the two arrays would contain:

MXRAY: 4 37 64 9 10
YXRAY: 12 19 1 −9 55 20 4 −8 52 56 56 1 52

MBIAS, YBIAS

The first element of MBIAS and YBIAS contains a count of the number of squares adjacent to each of the kings. This is followed by a list of all such squares.

THE SWAP-OFF ALGORITHM

After his recent game against the Russian program Kaissa, David Levy wrote 'In tactical situations it saw quite a lot but chess is primarily not a tactical game'. Chess experts have been making similar statements to chess programers for at least ten years and have been largely ignored — why?

Figure 3

We believe that chess is primarily a tactical game and we suspect that the disagreement is due either to a different definition of tactics by the two groups, or else the chess players sublimate the tactics that every program has to handle in some way or other. We have not always held this view but have been forced to accept it after experimenting with a purely positional tree searcher. If one examines the Levy-Kaissa game for example, of the 63 positions reached, only the first five had no pieces *en prise*. We would therefore claim that at least 58 of the positions required some tactical analysis.

Chess players probably maintain a tactical balance subconsciously and it is only when this balance is disturbed that the move is considered tactical. However, if a computer is to play a semblance of a sensible game of chess it has to maintain this balance by some device or other. This, we believe, is why pure tree-searchers have in the past tended to outperform positional programs. In MASTER we try to maintain this tactical balance by:

(a)   Computing swap-offs on the squares of each piece.
(b)   Extreme pessimism at the final ply evaluation.
(c)   Forcing all captures and checks into the tree search.

However, before swap-offs can be computed, it is necessary to record whether or not pieces can actually take part in exchanges. Without this, serious errors can occur. For example, the position given in figure 3 was reached by MASTER in a game using a very early version of the swap-off on squares algorithm. MASTER considered the knight on g4 to be defended by the bishop on d7 and therefore considered d1-g4 to be a bad move for White. When the algorithm was modified to remove the offensive and defensive role of the pinned bishop on d7, the program considered that the bishop on b5 needed no protection and so considered moving the knight from c3. The algorithm had to be modified again to allow an offensive role for the d7 bishop on the square of the pinning piece, i.e. b5.

The abilities of the pieces to attack or defend other pieces are defined by two logical arrays, OFEN and DEFEN, which are initialised as TRUE and then modified as follows. (Note the effect of tempo in these patterns. In each case 'I' have just moved and your pieces are therefore free to initiate a capture sequence.)

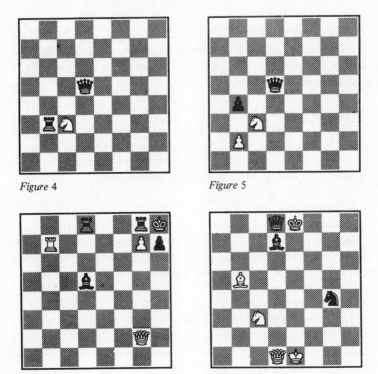

Figure 4

Figure 5

Figure 6

Figure 7

1. You threaten my piece and I do not defend it, therefore OFEN = FALSE for my piece, e.g. for the position given in figure 4 my knight does not threaten your queen.

2. You threaten my piece by a lower valued piece, therefore OFEN = FALSE for my piece, e.g. for the position given in figure 5 my knight does not attack your queen.

3. You threaten my piece by an equal or lower valued piece, or I do not defend it and you are not in check, DEFEN = FALSE for my piece, e.g. for the position given in figure 6 the queen on g2 and the rook on b7 are both attacked by the lower-valued bishop on d5. DEFEN should therefore be FALSE for both of these pieces. However, the black king is in check, and both the rook and the queen can therefore defend the pawn on g7.

4. For pieces pinned to pieces of larger value than the pinning piece, or pinned to inadequately defended pieces, OFEN and DEFEN = FALSE, except for an offensive role on the square of the pinning piece, e.g. for the position given in figure 7 the bishop on d7 does not defend the knight on g4 from attack by the queen on d1. It can, however, take part in swap-offs on the square of the pinning bishop on b5.

ANALYSIS PHASE

Having set up information in the various arrays during the synthesis phase, the program proceeds to analyse features of the position by extracting the relevant information.

Material Value

The value of each piece is read from arrays giving the value of each type of piece on each square of the board. This allows us to encourage knights to go to the centre of the board rather than the edges and to give an incentive for bishops to go to knight 2, for example.

Square Control

Control of squares is measured rather roughly by comparing MYCONTROLS and YRCONTROLS for each square of the board. The value of controlling a particular square is read from an array of values. The centre squares of the board are rated much higher than the edge squares.

Threats and Swap-Offs

The arrays MYCONTROLS, YRCONTROLS, MYPIECES and YRPIECES are used to compute scores for attacking defended pieces. If 'I' have just moved, then your threat to my pieces scores higher than my threat to your pieces. Thus I will get a positive score for attacking your bishop with my knight, but a negative score for attacking your bishop with a bishop (my threat to your bishop minus your threat to my bishop).

The same arrays are used in conjunction with the OFEN and DEFEN arrays to compute the value in pawns gained by swapping off on the squares of all the pieces except the kings. The algorithm allows the choice of stopping the swap sequence or continuing, for each side when it is their turn to move. This threat to capture material, in units of pawns, is multiplied by a suitable factor dependent upon the depth in the search tree.

At all plies but the final one, the factor is about half the true value of a pawn, for each unit for both sides. At the final ply a much more pessimistic value is used. With your threat and my threat values equal to half a pawn, then it will consider capturing a pawn, threatening to capture a pawn and protecting a threatened pawn equally valuable.

X-rays, etc.

The MXTH and YXTH arrays are examined to compile values for pins, skewers and X-rays.

Attacks on the Kings

The MBIAS and YBIAS arrays are used to analyse the strength of attacks on the respective kings. The more powerful the pieces controlling the squares and the greater the number of squares controlled the greater the threat. Again tempo is taken into account so that your attack scores higher than mine.

Figure 8

Pawn Structure

Various arrays are used to store information about pawns. These are analysed to give values for pawn structure, passed pawns, rooks on open files, the relationship between kings and pawns in the end game etc.

FORCING MOVES AND KEY SQUARES

Like many programs, we force into the tree search all captures and checks no matter how low their static evaluation, but they are kept in the order designated by the static evaluation. These are not, however, the only moves forced into the tree, we also force in certain moves that increase control over key squares.

Most of these key squares are discovered by the CHKTST routine (Birmingham and Kent 1980) which is used to detect mates or mating sequences statically. CHKTST is called to provide further analysis whenever a move is found which puts the opponent in check. Apart from recognising checkmates and positions from which mate can be forced, it also recognises positions that are nearly checkmate.

In the position given in figure 8, f1-f8 is a checking move and therefore automatically invokes CHKTST. This discovers that the move would be mate except that the rook is attacked by the king and is not defended. The square f8 is therefore marked as a 'Key Square' and all moves are examined to see if they increase control on this square. Any moves that do increase control on the Key Square are forced into the tree for further analysis, no matter how low their static evaluation. For example, the following moves would be forced in: b3-a3, b3-b4, b3-b8, b3-f3, e5-g7 and e5-d6. This last move looks terrible from the point of view of the static evaluator as it leaves both the queen and the bishop attacked and not defended and yet the move wins the game.

Other Key Squares found by CHKTST are the squares of your pieces which defend the square on which I wish to mate. Using the arrays already described, this is a simple table look-up, i.e.

YRSQ(1) is the square containing your king

MYPIECES(1, YRSQ(1)) is the square containing my checking piece

Figure 9

Figure 10

YRPIECES(1, MYPIECES(1, YRSQ(1))) is the square containing your first piece that attacks my checking piece

In the position given in figure 9, g5-g8 is a checking move and therefore causes CHKTST to be called. This finds that the move would be mate if it was not for the black rook on f8. The square f8 is therefore recorded as a Key Square and all moves that increase control of this square are forced into the list. Eventually the move f7-d5 will be examined and found to lead to a win.

Other moves are forced in from analysis of the YBIAS array. Whenever every square round your king is attacked or blocked, then any move which increases my control over one or more of your YBIAS squares is forced into the tree. In the position given in figure 10, the move e6-d8 completes the net round the black king by increasing control on the f7 square from 0 to 1. This move is therefore forced into the list to be searched and is found to lead to a win, after d7-e5, e2-e5, f6-e5, d1-g1, etc.

THE STRATEGY ROUTINE

After each move MASTER calls a routine to see if its overall strategy should be changed. To change the strategy the program modifies several of the arrays that are used to compute the position evaluation.

1. The value of the centre squares falls as the game proceeds.

2. The program is encouraged to start a king-side or queen-side attack by increasing the value of controlled squares on that side of the board and by increasing the incentive to advance the king-side or queen-side pawns.

3. Since MASTER is weaker at endgames than the middle game, the value of a draw is increased as the pieces are exchanged.

4. An end game switch comes on when one side has lost more than half his material. The king is then encouraged to move to the centre and various other parameters are changed, e.g. the passed pawn value is doubled

5. Various special endgames are looked for and the arrays modified accordingly: (a) king and pawns v king and pawns; (b) king and pieces v king and pieces; (c) king and pieces v king; (d) king, bishop and knight v king.

The king, bishop and knight v king (KBNK) endgame is a good ex-

85	85	73	57	35	30	1	1
85	90	80	70	55	47	42	1
73	80	100	90	80	42	47	30
57	70	90	110	90	80	55	35
35	55	80	90	110	90	70	57
30	47	42	80	90	100	80	73
1	42	47	55	70	80	90	85
1	1	30	35	57	73	85	85

Figure 11

Figure 12

ample of how the program can be made to play a long-term strategy by modifying the arrays. From the worst position it takes over thirty moves with best play to win. First the king and pieces move into the centre of the board and drive the solitary king out. He is then forced to the edge of the board. As he can only be mated in the two corners that can be controlled by the bishop, he will usually run first to one of the other corners. He is then driven along the edge to one of the correct corners and mated. At one point he can make a run for it and get as far as bishop 3 before being caught and brought back under control.

To play this endgame the strategy routine swaps the king table to give a bias towards the correct corners of the board. Figure 11 gives the king table for the KBNK endgame for the king to be mated in either a1 or h8. Other factors that had to be modified were:

(a) The incentive to move the kings together was increased.

(b) The knight was encouraged to stay next to the king.

(c) The bishop was encouraged to stay away from the king.

(d) Control of squares adjacent to the king was increased in value.

(e) The positional value of the king, using the table in figure 11, was made equal to the sum of the square containing the king and the highest-valued square not controlled by the opponent.

In his book on endgames Fine gives the position in figure 12 and demonstrates a win in 32 moves. We set up this position and let the program play both sides with a 7-ply lookahead. It averaged less than 10 seconds per move on a 370/168.

1.	Kc5-c4	Bh5-e2	11.	Kg7-h8	Ke5-f6
2.	Kc4-c5	Na1-b3	12.	Kh8-g8	Bd3-e4
3.	Kc5-d5	Ka5-b4	13.	Kg8-h8	Ne6-g5
4.	Kd5-e5	Kb4-c3	14.	Kh8-g8	Ng5-f7
5.	Ke5-e4	Kc3-c4	15.	Kg8-f8	Be4-h7
6.	Ke4-e5	Nb3-c5	16.	Kf8-e8	Nf7-e5
7.	Ke5-f5	Kc4-d4	17.	Ke8-d8	Kf6-e6
8.	Kf5-f6	Be2-d3	18.	Kd8-c7	Ne5-d7
9.	Kf6-f7	Kd4-e5	19.	Kc7-c6	Bh7-d3
10.	Kf7-g7	Nc5-e6	20.	Kc6-c7	Bd3-e4

21.	Kc7-d8	Ke6-d6	28.	Kb8-a7	Bd5-c4
22.	Kd8-e8	Be4-d5	29.	Ka7-b8	Bc4-a6
23.	Ke8-d8	Nd7-f6	30.	Kb8-a8	Kc6-b6
24.	Kd8-c8	Nf6-e8	31.	Ka8-b8	Ne6-d4
25.	Kc8-b8	Ne8-c7	32.	Kb8-a8	Ba6-b7
26.	Kb8-c8	Nc7-e6	33.	Ka8-b8	Nd4-c6
27.	Kc8-b8	Kd6-c6		Mate	

Although the program made some weak moves in both attack and defence, it is clear that its strategic play was good. Also, in a match, one is allowed up to three minutes per move on average which would allow the program to use a 9-ply search, which corrects most of the weak moves.

REFERENCES

Birmingham, J.A. & P. Kent (1977) Tree searching and tree pruning techniques, in *Advances in Computer Chess 1* (ed M.R.B.Clarke). Edinburgh: University Press.

Slagle, J.R. (1971) *Artificial Intelligence. The Heuristic Programming Approach.* McGraw Hill.

Beal, D.F. (1980) An analysis of minimax (this volume).

Bell, A.G. (1973). Computer Chess Experiments, in *Computer Chess*, Proceedings of a one-day meeting on Chess Playing by Computer, Atlas Computer Laboratory, Science Research Council, Chilton, Didcot, Oxon.

Birmingham, J.A. & P. Kent (1980) Mate at a glance (this volume).

Bell, A.G. (1970) How to program a computer to play legal chess. *Computer J. 13*, 208-19.